CHOOSING TOMORROW'S DOCTORS

Edited by Isobel Allen, Philip Brown, Patricia Hughes

The publishing imprint of the independent
Policy Studies Institute
100 Park Village East, London NW1 3SR
Tel. 0171 468 0468   Fax. 0171 388 0914

© **in this volume Policy Studies Institute and St George's
Hospital Medical School, 1997**

ISBN 0 85374 729 6

PSI report number 844

Typesetting by PCS Mapping & DTP, Newcastle upon Tyne
Printed and bound in Great Britain by
Redwood Books, Trowbridge, Wiltshire

CONTENTS

PREFACE

This book brings together the papers from a conference held in May 1996 at Senate House, University of London, entitled *Choosing Tomorrow's Doctors*. The conference was part of the Edward Jenner bicentenary celebrations organised by St George's Hospital Medical School.

In 1993 the General Medical Council produced a document called *Tomorrow's Doctors* which has far-reaching implications for doctors and for medical education. In a fast-changing society we must confront the fact that the future role of doctors is no longer entirely predictable. The aim of the conference was to stimulate doctors and others to reflect both on their own experience of medicine today and on the issues we must consider as we select the doctors of tomorrow.

The conference was therefore presented in two parts. The first half of the programme addressed the question of what we select doctors for: to fill a role in society, to be effective with their patients, and to enjoy a satisfying job. The second half focused on the selection of medical students and specifically looked at problems of prediction and related ethical issues.

The conference generated a great deal of interest, and over 200 people attended. These were from both within and outside the medical profession, and included secondary school tutors, many medical school deans, teachers, students, and representatives of professional bodies. They were rewarded with a lively range of presentations from a highly distinguished panel of speakers.

We are grateful to the St George's staff who so ably chaired the conference sessions: Professor Sir William Asscher, Dr Gillian Farnsworth, Dr Patricia Hughes and Professor Sean Hilton. We should also like to acknowledge the willing help which the following people gave in organising the conference: Sir Colin Dollery, Pro-Vice Chancellor for Medicine; Mr David Eames, Secretary/Registrar of the Faculty of Medicine; Mrs Susan Gove, Chief Librarian, SGHMS; Professor Kenneth Hobbs, Dean of Faculty of Medicine.

Isobel Allen
Philip Brown
Patricia Hughes

THE EDWARD JENNER BICENTENARY

1996 marked the bicentenary of the first vaccination against smallpox by Edward Jenner, who trained at St George's Hospital, London. The conference, *Choosing Tomorrow's Doctors*, was organised by the School as part of the celebrations.

Edward Jenner was born in Berkeley, Gloucestershire, the youngest son of the Reverend Stephen Jenner, vicar of Berkeley. Following the death of his parents when he was five, he was brought up by his older brother and an aunt. In 1763, Jenner was sent as an apprentice to a local doctor, John Ludlow, where he remained for six years.

In 1770, at the age of 21, Jenner enrolled as a student at St George's Hospital as a pupil of John Hunter, who remained a lifelong friend and correspondent. Hunter recommended Jenner for the job of cataloguing the thousands of specimens which Captain Cook brought back from Australia.

Jenner returned to Berkeley to work as a general practitioner in 1773 but continued to exercise his scientific curiosity in many directions, producing diverse papers including one on ballooning, and a famous study of the life of the cuckoo. In 1783 he met his future wife, Catherine Kingscote, and they married in 1788.

In 1796, Jenner inoculated a local child, James Phipps, with matter from a cowpox pustule from a local milkmaid, Sarah Nelmes. One month later, he inoculated James with variola without ill effect. Jenner presented these results in a paper to the Royal Society. The paper was refused, so Jenner privately published a book, *An Inquiry into the Causes and Effects of Variola Vaccinae, a disease discovered in some of the Western Counties of England particularly Gloucestershire, and known by the name of the Cow-Pox.*

Medical opinion was divided about the value of the new procedure but, despite some vigorous opposition, support for vaccination spread. Jenner's work received royal approval in 1800, when he was presented to the King and Queen, and in 1806 he received a substantial grant from Parliament.

Following the death of his wife in 1815 Jenner returned to Berkeley where he continued his general practice and his vaccination work. He continued to spend one day a week vaccinating the poor free of charge. He died of a stroke in 1823 and is buried with his wife and eldest son in Berkeley Church.

THE CONTRIBUTORS

Isobel Allen

Isobel Allen is Head of Social Care and Health Studies at the Policy Studies Institute, an independent research institute. Her own main research interests are in doctors' careers and the organisation of the medical workforce; in older people; and in family planning and related issues, especially to do with teenage pregnancies. She has also been responsible for evaluations of various health service initiatives for homeless people, midwifery group practices and family planning and pregnancy counselling projects for young people. She is managing and evaluating a major initiative for the Department of Health – Caring for People who Live at Home. She has particular expertise in the interface between health and social care. In addition, she is a Non-Executive Member of Enfield and Haringey Health Authority.

Tessa Blackstone

Baroness Blackstone is Master of Birkbeck College in the University of London. In the House of Lords she has been the frontbench opposition spokesman first on education and then on foreign affairs. She was educated at the London School of Economics, where she received her PhD in 1969. After nine years as a Lecturer in Social Administration at the LSE, she became, in 1975, a member of the Central Policy Review Staff in the Cabinet Office. In 1978 she became Professor of Educational Administration at the University of London Institute of Education, and then from 1983–87 was first Deputy Education Officer (Resources) and then Clerk to the Authority and Director of Education at the Inner London Education Authority. In 1987 Tessa Blackstone became a Labour Life Peer. She is the author of many articles on social and education policy, and also of a number of books.

Philip Brown

Philip Brown is Curriculum Development Facilitator at St George's Hospital Medical School, London. Philip read history at the University of Leeds, and in 1981 started his career in educational administration at the Council for National Academic Awards. He then spent six years at the University of London's Senate House, where he was a senior examinations administrator. Philip joined St George's in 1991 as Deputy Academic Registrar, concerned with many areas including educational planning and development. In his current post he is responsible for co-ordinating the design and implementation of the School's new undergraduate medical curriculum, which started in 1996, and he also co-organises, with Patricia Hughes, teaching courses for doctors.

Kenneth Calman

Sir Kenneth Calman is Chief Medical Officer in the Department of Health. He graduated from the University of Glasgow in 1967. He was formerly Professor of Oncology in Glasgow before becoming Dean of Postgraduate Medicine and Professor of Postgraduate Medical Education. He was appointed Chief Medical Officer at the Scottish Home and Health Department and then took up the post of CMO at the Department of Health in 1991. He is a Fellow of numerous Royal Colleges and Faculties and in 1979 was elected a Fellow of the Royal Society of Edinburgh. He has written many books and scientific papers. Sir Kenneth has a number of outside interests including the history of medicine, Scottish literature, cartoons and gardening.

Joe Collier

Joe Collier is Reader and Consultant in Clinical Pharmacology at St George's Hospital Medical School and has been active in selecting medical students for over twenty years. He is Chair of the Medical School's Equal Opportunities Committee and is Clinical Secretary of the Health Authority's Local Research Ethics Committee. He edits the Drug and Therapeutic Bulletin, a monthly magazine published by the Consumers Association and sent free to doctors throughout the UK.

John Collins

John Collins is Associate Professor of Surgery at the University of Auckland in New Zealand. After training in the UK he moved to New Zealand in the 1970s, since when he has had a considerable interest in medical student selection. His MD thesis was on the selection and assessment of medical students.

Sally Greengross

Sally Greengross, OBE, is Chief Executive of Age Concern England. Author of numerous books and articles, she writes, lectures and broadcasts frequently, both in the UK and elsewhere, on a wide range of issues concerning policy and practice relating to older people. Her earlier background included lecturing, research and work with children, families and young offenders. She is Joint Chairman of the Board of the Age Concern Institute of Gerontology, King's College, and is a Fellow of the Royal Society of Arts and Royal Society of Health. As well as being a member of several ministerial committees she is also Patron of Home Concern, President of Action on Elder Abuse, Secretary General of Eurolink Age and Vice-President for Europe of the International Federation on Ageing. Lady Greengross was voted UK Woman of Europe in 1990.

Robert Hale
Robert Hale is Director and Consultant Psychotherapist at the Portman Clinic. He is also a Consultant Psychotherapist at the Tavistock Clinic where he was formerly Dean of Postgraduate Studies. In 1996 he was appointed North Thames Region Associate Dean in charge of career development and counselling for doctors in need of psychological help.

Patricia Hughes
Patricia Hughes is Senior Lecturer and Consultant in Psychological Medicine at St George's Hospital Medical School. She trained in psychiatry in Glasgow and London and in psychoanalysis at the Institute of Psychoanalysis. She is an accidental educationalist, who complained about poor training in teaching for doctors and thus became Senior Lecturer in Medical Education. She believes that acceptable working conditions for doctors should begin and be modelled with decent teaching of medical students.

Chris McManus
Chris McManus is Professor of Psychology at Imperial College School of Medicine at St Mary's and at University College London, where he came via Cambridge, Birmingham, and Bedford College, London. He has a long-standing interest in issues around medical student selection.

Peter Richards
Peter Richards was Dean of St Mary's Hospital Medical School from 1979 until 1995. In 1988 he was largely responsible for the merger of St Mary's with Imperial College to form Imperial College of Science, Technology and Medicine. In 1995 he became Medical Director of the Northwick Park and St Mark's NHS Trust. Through his time as Dean of St Mary's he researched prospectively with Chris McManus into many aspects of medical student selection.

WELCOMING ADDRESS

Professor Andrew Rutherford, Vice-Chancellor,
University of London

When Rudyard Kipling spoke at a dinner at the Middlesex Hospital in 1908, he began, 'Gentlemen – it may not have escaped your professional observation that there are only two classes of mankind in the world – doctors and patients... Speaking as a patient,' he went on, 'I should say that the average patient looks upon the average doctor very much as a non-combatant [in war time] looks upon the troops fighting on his behalf . The more trained men there are between his body and the enemy the better.' But what sort of training do these men – and women – need, and how are they to be selected for that role?

The General Medical Council's Education Committee set a milestone in December 1993 with its publication of new recommendations on undergraduate medical education under the title *Tomorrow's Doctors*. In introducing its recommendations, the Education Committee drew attention to the changing demands of health care delivery which have intensified progressively over the course of the last century. Many of these changes have been externally driven, brought about for example by the ageing population, and in more recent years by the application of new biomedical sciences and new clinical techniques, the growth also in the public understanding of disease and disability, and the growing interest of the population in the health of the public and the individual.

The ever-expanding demands on health care have led to an almost exponential growth in the knowledge base of medicine and an expectation that our doctors must carry all this knowledge in their heads in the practice of their profession. I was interested to learn that even as long ago as 1863 the General Medical Council noted a tendency to overloading of the curriculum in medical education, and that in 1876 Thomas Huxley observed that 'the burden we place on the medical student is far too heavy and it takes some doing to keep from breaking his intellectual back'. This message has been echoed over the succeeding years by many distinguished authorities.

The new enlightened approach of the GMC Education Committee recognises the undesirability and sheer impracticability of continuing to burden our medical students with the passive acquisition of ever-expanding quantities of knowledge. It places the emphasis instead on preparing doctors who can think for themselves and adapt to change, and who have attitudes to learning suited to the continuation of the educational process throughout their professional lives.

New undergraduate curricula, which reflect the philosophy of the Education Committee and recognise the continuum between the undergraduate educational process and postgraduate and continuing medical education, are now being developed and implemented throughout the country. But a critical part of this intensive and challenging process of change is to determine how best to identify the young or not so young people who will be suited in both intellect and personality to the new style of medical education and to the demands of the modern world for effective health care delivery.

Society places a special burden of responsibility on the nation's medical schools to select the right students for the long and demanding educational process. Not only do we make an enormous financial investment in the education of our doctors, but more important we all, unless we are very lucky, sooner or later depend on their wide range of competencies for our personal health and well-being and that of the nation as a whole. Not having had a medical education myself, I am only too acutely aware of how essential it is from the patient's point of view to have confidence in the understanding and skills of the medical profession when I am obliged to submit myself to their care.

The subject of this conference is of the very first importance; the timing is well-chosen; and we are grateful to all who have agreed to contribute to it.

INTRODUCTION

Sir William Asscher, Principal,
St George's Hospital Medical School

In October 1770 a remarkable event happened at St George's Hospital, Hyde Park Corner. John Hunter, father of modern surgery, accepted Edward Jenner as his student at St George's Hospital Medical School. Jenner's later achievements are well known, both as a caring general practitioner in Berkeley, Gloucestershire, and as the instigator of vaccination against smallpox precisely 200 years ago. We at St George's are very proud of him as one of our alumni. What it shows is that, like other medical schools, we get our student selection right some of the time. Today we are here to discuss how we can get it right more of the time.

What evidence is there that we have a problem? Firstly there are drop-outs from medical schools. These are not only expensive but also saddening because they deny a place to applicants that have been turned away. Then there are complaints from patients and particularly from the elderly and their relatives, concerning a lack of caring medicine and lack of communication skills shown by the doctors we graduate. The enormous loss of medical graduates in the early years after graduation is a further cause for concern. Presently it is being quantified by the British Medical Association. It is estimated to be in the order of 25 per cent per annum – a figure which I suspect is exaggerated since it includes temporary losses, particularly of women doctors wanting to start their family. Finally, as any dean of a medical school would tell you, there are problems that arise from a lack of uniformity of the selection processes and from their arbitrariness. In my mail in August each year is a steady stream of letters of complaint from disappointed applicants and their parents, friends of applicants and even their members of parliament.

There is undoubtedly a need to re-examine the selection procedures for medical students. Probably most of us would agree that the
quality of the entry determines the kind of doctor we produce, more
than the curriculum to which we subject them. Yet in most medical
schools it takes only ten or fifteen minutes of a perfunctory interview
to select a doctor in this country. I recall that when I was about to
become an officer in the Royal Engineers it took the War Office
Selection Board three days to determine whether I was fit to become
an officer and gentleman! Our procedures clearly need to satisfy
patients. They also need to satisfy our employers, the Health Service,
as well as our own professional standards. And finally, and not least,
the criteria should ensure that practising doctors themselves are going
to feel happy in the job they are doing. The demands of all these
interested parties do not always coincide but, in the selection of
students, we must never forget the infinite variety of doctors that are
needed to run an effective Health Service. With regard to the latter, I
have always been saddened by the way some distinguish between
academic doctors and Health Service doctors, or between those who
practise 'proper' medicine and those who are more remote from clinical work. Such antitheses in medicine are anathema to me because all
of us in the profession try to pursue the one and only type of medicine
that I know, namely *caring* medicine.

THE FUTURE OF MEDICAL PRACTICE

Kenneth Calman

The topic of this conference is important and my brief is to set some issues in context and perhaps give some personal views about what is important to me. I begin, of course, with Edward Jenner. The issue that comes out when you look at Jenner was his own medical education. It was very much an apprenticeship, it certainly was very practical, and having done some work, first of all in Gloucestershire, he came to London to work with John Hunter. He had enormous curiosity but he also had in the background a form of mentoring. The correspondence between Hunter and Jenner was fascinating and very important. He had many of the things which I think some of us would like to see at present but perhaps, most of all, his practice was very much about patient care and that is where he got his experience. That is a theme to which I will return.

I suppose if I was asked to say what I wanted from a doctor in the future, I would be looking for somebody who is a clinician, a scientist and a scholar. Let me try and take these a little bit further. What is required is quite difficult to define and asking the public what they want of the doctor will give you a wide variety of views. I suspect that we need a range of doctors who will supply a whole range of different needs. In terms of what medical education is for, then, the definition I use is 'to produce a doctor who will provide a high quality service both to the individual and the community, who will continue to learn and develop professionally through his or her career, who will assess personal performance regularly and seek continually to improve the service provided by research and development'. And, of course, all of that should occur within the context of the team approach. That may be too broad and I suspect that one of the issues that you will discuss today is what the objective of medical education really is. It returns all the time, I think, to clinical practice and the relationship between the patient and the doctor and how that relationship is cemented and developed.

Clinical skills

So let me take the first of my themes: clinical skills. This, I think, is sometimes forgotten in the big debates about what doctors do. What I suspect patients want are doctors who have sufficient clinical skills to make a diagnosis and to suggest treatment. The age-old history taking, inspection and clinical examination still remains for me very important. When I talk to some of my highly specialised colleagues who get patients referred with pleural effusions first diagnosed on Magnetic Resonance Imaging then I wonder whether things have gone too far. Clinical skills remain important. Interaction between patients and the doctor is perhaps the most important part of this and I have no doubt at all that British medical education is good because it provides that interaction from a very early stage in the course. But it does raise some very fundamental questions about what you want at the end of the day. Is it a specialist you want or is it a generalist? Most of the specialties right now are grappling with that issue, partly because it is about who is going to staff the front door of the hospital. If we have too many vascular surgeons or breast cancer specialists, who is going to deal with the patient as a whole? I think this is a very fundamental issue for medical education. Patients are often subjected to fairly large numbers of doctors during an episode in hospital and it must be very difficult for them sometimes to work their own way through this maze of medical skill and expertise.

It is undoubtedly about communication skills too. I think this is so fundamental to being a doctor that somehow we have to ensure not only that these skills are part of the course, (I don't mean that I have just done my week's communication skills – 'tick'), but that it is signalled up as something that is fundamental to clinical practice.

The other fundamental thing about the undergraduate course is whether the emphasis is in terms of health or in terms of illness. In practical terms it must be about illness, but in the long term the implications for the health of the population you look after is clearly important too. The medical profession are now beginning to debate this issue more than they did a little while ago and hence the importance for me of initiatives like *The Health of the Nation*.

Ethical issues continue to crop up and I raise it because I think the way in which Edward Jenner dealt with James Phipps could well be considered unethical in that he vaccinated him, then directly infected him with smallpox a month later. I am not sure whether that would get through St George's Ethical Committee right now. I suspect that it would not. It is interesting, however, that these issues have been around for a long time. They become, I think, more complicated but therefore even more important. The continuing education beyond the recognition that the undergraduate course is only a five year part of a forty year programme is also important, and that raises the issue about cramming too much in too quickly.

All of this comes down to a holistic approach not only to education but also to patient care, an approach of teamworking, recognising the importance of other disciplines and specialties, and common sense which I think is one of the more fundamental characteristics of doctors. I will not discuss in any detail the education and training issues, but there are just a couple of points that I want to make.

First, I believe quite strongly in education as opposed to training. To be trained is to have arrived – to be educated is to continue to travel. One of the reasons why I think that medical education is part of a university, as opposed to some other kind of organisation, is that the educational component for me is fundamental.

The second issue is about teaching the teachers and whether we have spent sufficient time in doing that. It is assumed that, because you are a clever person and a doctor in particular, teaching is a natural skill. I think that that is not necessarily the case. The quality of teaching is something we need to look at.

Lots of new clinical skills need to be developed, from teamworking, management, information technology to the importance of leadership. Having been a Dean myself some time ago, the ability to introduce extra topics into the curriculum is extraordinarily difficult as anybody in this audience I am sure will recognise. So somehow we have to free up time for people to think beyond some of the details. At the end of the day it must be about the development of competence, and I think in educational terms that may be one of the more important questions that we have to look at. Certainly in postgraduate terms the new training reforms will have that as their basis, and at the end of the period of time it is the assessment of competence that matters, following which continuing education can clearly evolve. So my first theme is that clinical skills remain extremely important.

The importance of science

My second theme is that science is also important and that research is fundamental. It takes me back to Jenner again and the importance of curiosity. Jenner was curious about everything and his writings about cuckoos and various other topics are remarkable. We need to ensure during the medical undergraduate course that we retain the spirit of curiosity and indeed develop it. Research for its own sake is not always terribly helpful and sometimes, I think, the research that people do is inappropriate and badly thought out. It is the skill of critically appraising a particular project which is important. What has become much more interesting recently is the issue of the certainty of science: that science must always be right and that the doctor in a white coat, particularly if he is called professor, must be correct.

Over the centuries the concept of disease has changed. There have been many different theories about disease: from disease being caused by humours to being clearly a mechanistic problem – the body as a machine – to being a molecular issue. I think perhaps at the moment a slightly more holistic approach is being adopted, but the way in which we interpret illness and disease has changed significantly. Given another opportunity I might use this as the title of an interesting talk that 'the history of medicine is the reclassification of disease'. The evidence basis is important. I do not think that is a particularly new concept to an audience like this but it is an important one. There is also the importance of outcomes and effectiveness – again not new concepts – but clearly the public wish to be more aware of what is going on, and for that reason I think that medical schools, scientists and doctors have to think much more about public understanding and public involvement in science.

The value of scholarship

My third theme is one which Jenner also took up in his poems and I will just say a word or two about what I think is important here. Why should we be thinking more about scholarship and what is the value of thinking beyond just being a technician? A scholar is one whose knowledge is extensive and exact. That is, I think, fairly fundamental but with scholarship comes something else and that is wisdom, and 'wisdom is the principal thing, therefore get wisdom and with thy getting get understanding'. The enormous experience that senior physicians and surgeons and others have is something we must not take lightly. It has grown up over a considerable period of seeing many people who are well or ill. That wisdom, that ability to sort out what is important and what is not important, and to help people, is fundamental. Part of it is about the depth of knowledge. That is something that needs time and in these times of remarkable change in the NHS it is important that there is a time for people to develop this wisdom, understanding and experience. That is actually for most doctors what makes being a doctor worthwhile. Knowledge in itself therefore cannot be compartmentalised into portions. These educational analogies of concept mapping are relevant. The individual specialty – rheumatology, cardiology – develops knowledge in great detail about an individual part of the body or disease process. There is a larger map which takes you into the practice of medicine and an even bigger map which relates to other disciplines and an even bigger map which takes you into the areas in which the Vice-Chancellor has a particular interest, in relation to philosophy, literature and the arts. It is when you begin to think about issues like quality of life that you realise that these extra disciplines are also very important. Oliver Wendell Holmes in *The Professor at the Breakfast Table* said:

> 'The longer I live the more I am satisfied with two things. The first that the truest lives are those that are cut rose-diamond fashion with many facets. Secondly, that society in one way or another is always trying to grind us down to a single flat surface.'

Doctors have to think beyond medicine sometimes. It takes me into the areas of the humanities in clinical practice. I raise this because a little while ago I was involved with a professor of philosophy in setting up a course on literature and medicine for medical students. It covered a wide range of issues and books which were of non-medical or medical nature. This course continues until today and I give you one example, *The Cocktail Party* by T.S. Eliot. The first act is about people at a cocktail party talking but not listening, and for a fourth year medical student to say, 'That is actually what we do with patients isn't it?' shows enormous maturity and shows that the first class people that we bring into medicine have great wisdom if we were just able to develop it. If you have not read *The Magic Mountain* by Thomas Mann then you have not thought about tuberculosis. If you have not read Ibsen's *An Enemy of the People* then you will not be a good public health doctor. There is an enormous depth in such literature which I think is important; it does put people in touch with a range of emotions and feelings. It is very useful in teaching and learning and certainly for the doctor's relaxation.

Conclusion

So these are areas which I think may be important and the issue for me, and I hope for you today, is how these three strands come together in terms of the synthesis between the clinician, the scientist and the scholar, giving depth and breadth to it, and the ability to present to patients or to the public specialised knowledge about individual conditions in the context of wider values and, indeed, in the context of emotions and feelings. The implications of this conclusion are clear, and relate to the education of doctors. That, of course, is what this seminar is all about and I look forward to your conclusions. For me it is about putting medical education into a broad context within a wider sphere so that medical students and indeed those who teach them think beyond clinical practice at times to other issues. For that reason, looking ahead to the future of medical practice, it is conferences like this which will begin to set the tone and improve the quality of medical education.

Finally, if I had a few words to say at the end about the future of medical education it would be about maintaining excellence, an educationally broad experience, driven by science, involving patients and the public, the importance of clinical skills, the intelligence function, based on the needs of the individual patient and the public and having a strong basis in ethics and values. The medical student of the future will perhaps be different from the one of the past but the objective will be the same, that is to improve patient care.

Discussion from the floor

There was discussion of whether the three main themes developed by Sir Kenneth should be extended beyond the education of doctors and whether education for the whole health care team should be unified. One questioner commented that other health professionals were university educated and that the law now allowed them to do things which used to be the preserve of the medical profession. Sir Kenneth stressed his commitment to a liberal education and the idea of the university. He felt that the question of whether all health professional groups should be educated together needed to be closely examined. He thought that some medical schools were more ready to pursue multidisciplinary core development than others. In relation to the sharing of responsibilities with other professional groups he thought it was part of the job of the Dean to ensure the appropriate development of the quality of medical education and its relationship to other professional groups.

The question arose of whether medical education and medical careers had become so specialised and departmentalised that little room was left for a life outside medicine, particularly in pursuing the creative arts. Sir Kenneth Calman thought it important that doctors should not lose the opportunity and the time to remain creative. He felt that the profession should 'open up a bit and allow this enormous creativity' to flourish.

A speaker from the floor raised the point that there were big differences between Jenner's time and today. In the Jenner era there was 'a lot more time to read' whereas today the problem was how to telescope a lot of work into a shorter time frame which inevitably seemed to lead to concentrating on examinations. Sir Kenneth agreed that the curriculum was too full. He felt that there was a need to return to the philosophy of what was needed and to recognise that the undergraduate course was 'not the end of the world but the beginning of the world'.

The question arose of the extent to which present medical education in this country would be appropriate in the next century when it was likely that there would be much greater movement of doctors within Europe. Sir Kenneth noted that many of the recent changes in medical education had occurred because 'we are part of Europe'. He felt that at the specialty level we were leading Europe in many ways in terms of training and development but that at a government regulatory framework level there was a need for further development.

The central problem of how best to select medical students was discussed, with speakers from the floor raising the question of whether it might be better to move towards a system such as that in North America where medicine was a postgraduate course and students were more mature when they entered medical school. It was noted that three Australian medical schools were also considering becoming graduate schools because they felt they could 'select more rationally at that age'. Sir Kenneth thought that the debate over the extent to which the medical school course was too science based and whether a more liberal arts based course was preferable was one of the big issues for medical education. The question of whether medicine should be a postgraduate course would no doubt be discussed within the conference.

WHAT PATIENTS WANT
FROM THEIR DOCTORS

Sally Greengross

Doctors today and tomorrow are having to cope with immense change. As well as being people of sensitivity, and having the stamina and judgement that we have always expected from the medical profession, doctors need to be increasingly flexible in their approach to their clinical work. Those in the medical profession who teach and who build on their own experience also have to cope with change which may mean that the very foundations on which their teaching is based are open to question.

Changes in the delivery of health care

Demography

We are facing unprecedented changes in demography, and the speed of change is something we all find difficult to cope with. These changes were illustrated rather nicely for me once in the story of a man who went to his GP for a check-up. The GP examined him and said, 'Mr Jones you are *incredibly* fit for a man of 50,' whereupon Mr Jones replied, 'Who said I am 50? I'm 67!' The doctor then said, 'My goodness. That really is amazing. Do you mind if I ask you how old your father was when he died?' Mr Jones answered, 'Who said my father is dead? My father is 86; he drives or cycles to his office every day, goes on walking tours, climbs mountains and has a very good life.' The doctor said, 'Good heavens, what a family. May I ask you how old your grandfather was when he died?' Mr Jones replied, 'Who said my grandfather is dead? He is 104 and he is getting married in two weeks.' The doctor said, 'Getting married in two weeks? Why would a man of 104 want to get married?' And Mr Jones answered, 'Who said he *wants* to get married?'

Delivery of health care

The context in which people are living is changing and there is an increasing need for outreach care. Another important aspect of today's medicine is the close relationship which is now expected between specialists in different fields of medicine and GPs working in the community. A potential doctor needs to recognise the additional responsibilities now facing the medical profession. Doctors often work as successors to the parish priest, often as confidants, in a society which can no longer guarantee that what is heard or said will be treated as confidential. Decisions which used to be very much the responsibility of the doctor, may now become that of the law courts. Some decisions which were considered medical are now recognised as being much wider, encompassing social and other factors. In some cases, a training in philosophy rather than medicine might be more appropriate.

The relationship between hospital and community

The idea that medicine is increasingly part of the wider community it serves coincides with the switch to primary provision being the core of medical care, in contrast to the more hospital-orientated practice of the past. Although doctors still learn much in hospital and take this back to the community they also need involvement and training in the community right from the start. This need is now recognised, but does it in fact happen? If so, does it happen sufficiently?

Perhaps we should think again about the separation of different fields of medicine. For example, where does public health cross into other medical specialties, and should the study of public health be linked to the study of the environment itself? The future partners in health care might well need to include more than the traditional group: the doctor, the surgery and the hospital. They might include all the different professions that impinge on our lives, particularly in an urban environment.

What do patients want from their doctors?

The patient does not see problems in terms of which specialist to go to. What concerns him or her is that somebody will identify the *total* problem and deal with it correctly. This is particularly the case for older people, most of whose problems are multi-faceted – neither purely physical, nor simply medical. So if as a doctor you are really prepared to deal with all the problems that people bring to you, you must have a wide range of knowledge. Your education, your learning, has to cover more than 'pure' medicine to include how to cope with the other pressures of modern living.

The training of doctors should include overall strategies to give the doctor an understanding of all the areas that he or she has to cover, including where the cut-off points are, where the priorities really are, and what the public will accept in terms of limits. Moreover, doctors will soon have to accept the need to discuss such ethical issues with patients.

Honesty in their approach to patients is very important within clear parameters, without the type of 'secrets' that used to be accepted about expenditure limits, priorities and so on. If beds are available for some specialist medical care, but not for theirs, patients need to know why that is. Are priorities being given to some conditions or to some groups of people that they do not know about? We will have to 'come clean', if patients of the future are to be satisfied.

And of course there remains the issue of the *power* which doctors have over their patients. Many older people, in particular, do not really know how to address their doctor and get their point across. This must add to their confusion and anxiety when faced with an apparent mismatch between today's provision of an ever widening range of new treatments and their personal experience. What they hear, what they read and what they see on television may seem very different from what is happening to them.

Patient satisfaction

One very important fact has emerged from patient surveys. Most patients of all ages do express satisfaction with their health care, and both small-scale and national surveys still show a high level of patient satisfaction with their doctors. A 1988 Gallup survey showed that 80 per cent of people thought their doctor did a good job. Levels of satisfaction tend to be greater among older people than among younger and there is a remarkable amount of agreement about what older patients want from their GP. Patients are not necessarily satisfied with administrative procedures, particularly with regard to irritating issues such as the appointment system in the surgery or the referral system for the hospital.

How can we maintain and improve standards?

Communication in the GP surgery
The GP surgery itself is the first point of contact for the patient and we must continually monitor whether it *is* providing a high level of care. Dr. Calman made the point clearly that the doctor must encourage the patient to say what he or she wants to say. This is difficult if doctors are not trained to be good listeners or not trained to do something about what they hear. In many cases it means developing counselling skills, especially with older patients, to give people time and space to say what is really on their mind. You have to feel, as a patient, that the doctor is taking you seriously. We all know the old story, 'My knee hurts, doctor' 'Well, what can you expect at your age?' 'Well, my other knee is the same age'. But the 'What can you expect at your age?' statement is actually an example of a deeper problem of negative attitudes which do need to be overcome. The practical effect of age discrimination is differential treatment in regard to screening, some aspects of cardiac care and many other aspects of medicine. As the Chief Medical Officer knows, Age Concern is continually battling against such differential treatment, giving everybody at the Department of Health a hard time.

The holistic approach
A patient needs a doctor who will give them adequate time and an opportunity to elaborate on their symptoms and to voice their fears. It is the voicing of these fears that is perhaps the most important thing before the doctor turns back to the screen and taps out a prescription. To do this, a doctor must have a holistic approach. Bernard Isaacs, a geriatrician, once told his students that he had cured the incontinence of an elderly lady with a screwdriver. Everybody in his audience looked extremely uncomfortable, whereupon he explained that what he had done was to reverse the way the toilet door was hanging in the residential home where she lived so that she could get her wheelchair through. That cured her incontinence immediately! So we must understand that problems are not simply physical or mental health issues. They may involve the environment, which Bernard understood completely.

Clear explanation
People need a clear diagnosis and explanation covering the range of available treatments, particularly with regard to medication, its side effects and possible long-term effects. Surveys show that about 20 per cent of doctors do not explain these points very clearly.

We see rapid change in information dissemination and in information technology, in what we learn and in how we can find out about things. The answers doctors give to people have to relate to the real world as the patients see it, rather than being particles of information, given down from 'on high'. Doctors need to learn to translate technical information into language that patients can understand.

Information about local services
Information must be accessible and understandable to the broad range of patients who need it. The surgery really needs to be a 'one stop' shop, so the GP in the community should have knowledge of local networks and information, not just about where the local pharmacy is but also a range of other information that people need. Sick people and elderly people especially may be frail and tired and without sufficient energy to go 'shopping around' for whatever they need to know. The GP's surgery is one place that most people go to at some time and it would make an enormous difference if the surgery or health centre could provide that information resource.

A doctor who can accept mortality and death
People need to feel that the doctor can help them make sense of their suffering – a difficult task, especially in a secular society. It is not easy to help someone be reconciled to death if the fight for life is over. John Berger said, 'The doctor is the familiar of death and when we call for a doctor we are asking him to cure us and to relieve our suffering, but if he cannot cure us we are also asking him to witness our dying.'

Iona Heath quotes in her recent book, *The Mystery of General Practice*, 'This acceptance can be very difficult for hospital doctors to come to terms with, when they are busily trying to cure a particular disease, but a learned understanding of the individual patient's wishes can be the most significant contribution to an older person and the family in those last days of life.'

Accessibility
At a practical level, a patient needs a doctor who can be visited without too much difficulty. This is a problem for a significant minority of patients. For example, 10 per cent of people over the age of 65 do not find it easy to visit their doctor and the main reason given is that the surgery is too far away. Ensuring that patients can get to surgeries or hospitals should be of vital interest to every GP. Outreach work, including home visits, sometimes jointly with consultants, for those who cannot reach the surgery would help to make community care a reality, as is already happening in some areas. Home visits can also be a valuable way of making and keeping contact with patients.

The doctor–patient relationship

People value personal contact. Cartwright and Smith, in a recent survey, showed how much more satisfied people were if they knew their GP well. In the survey, 81 per cent of people thought that they were good at explaining things to the doctor because they knew him or her well, and 38 per cent said they weren't good at explaining because they did not know the GP well. But we are not sure how much this picture is changing. Is the family doctor who knows the patient well becoming a figure of the past? Will patients continue in future to be able to feel that the doctor is offering advice solely in that patient's best interest? Survey evidence we have on older people shows that their view of GP care is not changing, so we are still able to make sure that the excellent relationship between GPs and their older patients in this country continues.

Doctors must reflect on the impact of the 'Health Centre' approach on this standard and ensure that effective time management does not compromise this aspect of good care. One very elderly lady said recently, 'There are as many doctors here to choose from as checkouts in the supermarket, but you are always aware of the person behind you in the queue.' We must remind ourselves constantly that personal care is important and needs to be nurtured.

The integrity of the doctor-patient relationship

In the modern framework of the NHS with the purchaser/provider split how far will fund-holding GPs be allowed to be the advocate of the patient? There has always been resource constraint within the NHS, but it has not been so overt or at the level of the GP in quite the way it is now. The patient population will increasingly challenge the doctor on issues like discrimination and priorities going to certain groups of patients. GPs who must now look to their budgets when considering a test or a hospital referral will need to be openly accountable to their patients for their decisions, even if these decisions are against their better judgement. One of the greatest challenges for today's and tomorrow's doctors may be how to retain a trusting relationship with the patient

New initiatives

Surveys among older people show that the ability to stay fit and active is more important to them than anything else. My own organisation, Age Concern, is doing its bit to help give priority to keeping older people in good health. We know that there is a good deal of ignorance among GPs about the role and services provided by the voluntary sector and vice versa. The Department of Health recently collabo-rated with Age Concern to create the Griffiths Fellowship, in memory of Sir Roy Griffiths, and the present Fellow is studying how the volun-tary sector and local GP practices might collaborate. Voluntary bodies might, for example, have a base in a general practice or Health Centre to facilitate access and easy collaboration with GPs.

Ageing Well is another initiative which has the backing of govern-ment, industry, the World Health Organisation, the European Commission and the Health Education Authority. It is a programme of health promotion which uses older people as a key resource as trained Senior Health Mentors. The programme is tied to the Health of the Nation targets and its mentors are responsible for transmitting appropriate messages, and working with the medical and wider health care team. This multidisciplinary scheme is an example of the combined effort that we need to succeed in dealing with one of the greatest challenges at the end of the twentieth century, the ageing of the population.

Conclusion

To work as part of a team, to be able and prepared to continue to learn throughout one's career and, most important, to take on board both care for the individual and the community, are essential aspects of a doctor's role today. Many people inside and outside the profes-sion resent the politicisation of health care and how that impinges on their own lives. Doctors need to take this seriously and, as they themselves become increasingly politicised, liaise closely with patients to make their voices even stronger.

Discussion from the floor

In discussion, it was noted that patients' expectations derive largely from experience, but the increasing media attention to medicine and health care, both in its documentary format as well as its soap opera format, must have an influence on people's expectations both now and increasingly perhaps in the future. The expectations of all of us are very much higher than they were in the past. This demands greater honesty and openness.

It was acknowledged that a patient satisfaction rate of 80 per cent is high, but noted that although 80 per cent say they are satisfied that their doctor is doing a good job, 80 per cent *do not* say they are satisfied with what happens to them in the Health Service as a whole.

Finally, participants discussed the question of resources. Doctors of the future will see an ageing population, higher expectations, more ill people. How will we actually fund all this, and where will we get the people to do the work? Although there has been an influx of new medical students, as of this year there will be no added resources to go with them.

WHAT DOCTORS WANT
FROM THEIR CAREERS

Isobel Allen

Over the past ten years I have conducted a number of studies of doctors' careers in which the aim was to explore the motivation, experiences and aspirations of men and women doctors. My most recent study *Doctors and their Careers: a New Generation* was published at the end of 1994[1]. It was carried out to follow-up the findings of *Doctors and their Careers*[2, 3], a study funded and initiated by the Department of Health and published in 1988 with the aim of examining the implications for medical manpower planning of the fact that women would soon account for 50 per cent of medical qualifiers.

In that original research I looked at three cohorts of doctors who had qualified in 1966, 1976 and 1981. At the time that we interviewed them in 1986 they were aged on average 43, 33 and 28. We aimed at interviewing 100 men and 100 women from each of the years of qualifiers, and in the event we interviewed 640 men and women who were based all over the country.

In 1991 we followed up that research:

a) to see what had happened in the previous five years to the 1976 and 1981 medical qualifiers interviewed for *Doctors and their Careers*;
b) to compare a sample of 1986 medical qualifiers with their counterparts from previous cohorts;
c) to examine the extent to which opportunities for women doctors were seen to have changed since 1986; and
d) to examine in detail the question of part-time or less than full-time training and career posts in medicine.

In this paper I will refer to the study of 1986 qualifiers[1] which was based on personal interviews with 229 doctors (105 men and 124 women) who had qualified at medical schools in Great Britain. We interviewed them five years after qualification in 1991, at which time the average age of the doctors interviewed was 28, the same as their counterparts from the 1981 cohort whom we had interviewed five years earlier.

The profile of medical manpower has changed dramatically over the past ten years. Fifty per cent of those entering the medical profession are women and the proportion of women qualifiers has been over 40 per cent since the mid-1980s. One of the main aims of the first study was to see what constraints they were likely to encounter and how these could be alleviated or removed. But what we found was that many of the career constraints and difficulties experienced by women were also regarded as difficulties and constraints by men. I was struck more by the similarities between men and women doctors rather than the differences. The medical career structure as it existed back in 1986 was thought by doctors to be out-of-date and rigid and five years later little was perceived to have changed.

I would like to look at some of the messages from my research over the years, in particular those about factors affecting career choice, if one can use such an active word about decisions which often appear to have been made negatively rather than positively.

Why medicine at all?

Perhaps the first question to be asked in a paper with this title is why do doctors choose to study medicine in the first place?

In my first report on doctors' careers we examined in some detail the family and school background of the different cohorts of doctors and their reasons for studying medicine. There had been marked changes in the profile of doctors, with far fewer qualifiers from the younger cohorts coming from independent boarding schools, fewer from medical families and increasing proportions with very good A-level results. There were also indications that the 1966 women in particular were more likely than men to have been strongly motivated towards studying medicine, and to have made up their minds at an earlier stage that they wished to be doctors. These women had 'always wanted to be doctors', while quite a few of the men had drifted into medicine because they could not think of anything else to do or because their fathers were doctors.

However, there was clear evidence of a trend in the later cohorts, particularly among the men, of the qualifiers having decided to become doctors because they were good at science. We queried whether this was a particularly good basis for wanting to become a doctor, but concluded that it was probably no worse than wanting to do it because of sporting excellence or paternal influence.

In our earlier report we found that the 1981 qualifiers were much more likely to be critical of the medical career system that they had entered, not only because they were at a stage in their careers when doctors have traditionally been overworked and dissatisfied, but also because many of them felt that they might be in the wrong jobs, felt 'trapped' in medicine and were unhappy about their present jobs and future prospects, particularly in comparison with their contemporaries outside medicine. There was almost no careers advice on medicine at schools and most students had no idea what being a doctor entailed. Most doctors interviewed for both studies had had little idea of what they were letting themselves in for when they started at medical school, and the high level of regret found among the younger qualifiers was often a reflection of poor quality careers advice from home and school.

The trends noted in the first report continued among the 1986 qualifiers. They were almost as likely as the 1981 qualifiers to have studied medicine because they were good at science, but, more important, they were exceptionally good at science. The vast majority of the 1986 qualifiers had studied only science subjects at A-level, and their results were generally better than those of the 1981 qualifiers and considerably better than those of the 1976 qualifiers. But perhaps the most notable finding was the achievements at A-level of the women. 25 per cent of the 1986 women qualifiers had achieved three A grades or better in their A-levels, compared with 12 per cent of the 1986 men and 20 per cent of the 1981 men. The 1986 women were very high achievers in general, since over 40 per cent of them had achieved at least two As and a B at A-level. They were excellent mathematicians, with better results than the men. The mean scores of both men and women were higher among the 1986 qualifiers than among all their predecessors. But they were not only good at science – they had Grade 8 violin, clarinet – they had done masses of good works – they were interesting, intelligent, all-rounders. What was to become of them?

There was an increase in the proportions of 1986 qualifiers from state schools, and a particular increase in the proportions from comprehensive schools. There was a marked decline over the years in the proportion of qualifiers attending independent boarding schools. There was no doubt at all that the schooling of the 1986 qualifiers more closely reflected that of their contemporaries in society at large than that of their older counterparts had done. Perhaps this is one reason why they were so keen on leading 'a normal life'.

But this undoubtedly affected the profile of those entering the profession of medicine, and many of these more recent qualifiers were much less prepared, or able, to operate the traditional 'old boy' network referred to so often in my first report as being of enormous influence in career progression. It was quite apparent, in the course of our research, that we were beginning to see a certain clash of cultures, and it was by no means clear what kind of pattern would emerge in the future. There were, however, strong indications that being very clever and good at science at the age of 18 was no guarantee of continuing success in the competitive world of medicine.

The question arises of whether being good at science is necessarily a prerequisite for being a good doctor, or even whether good scientists make good – and happy – doctors. The 1986 qualifiers themselves were often not sure, but had usually felt there was little alternative. Most had not even considered the question at the time – 'Medical training was simply an extension of studying sciences...', but some had bitterly regretted it, and still did. 'It's a frightful price to pay for being good at science...' was the chilling remark of one woman doctor in my last study.

It may appear that there is a need to reconsider the selection of medical school students to ensure that people do not enter the medical profession just because they are good at science. Perhaps many of those who are good at science should become scientists, and attributes other than academic excellence at A-level science should be taken more seriously by medical school selectors. It is possible that much of the regret and loss of confidence found among a substantial proportion of the 1986 women qualifiers was related to the fact that they had chosen the wrong career, and had found themselves unable to change direction.

There is also a pressing need to look at the careers advice given to young people considering a career in medicine. The advice from schools was generally agreed to be either non-existent or discouraging, and almost always ill-informed according to our respondents in both studies. People were either encouraged to do medicine because they were good at science, or they were discouraged for all kinds of reasons, as one young woman psychiatric registrar put it in our last study: 'I was told I shouldn't apply by my headmaster and science teachers because I was a woman and because I came from a comprehensive school and because my father wasn't a doctor...'

It seems absurd that so many people enter medical school with so little real appreciation of what it entails. It costs nearly £200,000 to put a student through medical school, and such an investment should not be made on such little information.

But I would issue a warning that those selecting medical students do not select *out* those who may end up having regrets. Maybe they are the ones who will bring about necessary changes in a profession which many of our respondents described as being 'very conservative', with success going to 'conventional people with conventional careers'.

And similarly, do not select out all the brilliant scientists. Medicine needs brilliant scientists as well as caring, compassionate people. Perhaps they are sometimes the same people.

Medical school

The background of the qualifiers undoubtedly had far-reaching implications. But what about medical school? Doctors were still looking for careers advice and weren't finding much. We found in the last report that careers advice at medical school was usually thought to be almost as limited as that at school, although the later qualifiers had access to rather more formal careers information in the form of careers fairs than the earlier cohorts.

The main complaints about careers advice at medical school was that it was inadequate, inappropriate, not tailored to the personal requirements of the students, unrealistic about the demands of different specialties, and was particularly unsuitable for those who thought they might have made a mistake in studying medicine. There were widespread criticisms of a lack of a proper tutorial system, either to give personal support or for careers advice. But even if students knew that careers advice was available from tutors there was often a marked reluctance to take it up. We were given a lot of evidence that not all tutors were interested in their role. 'He was an anatomy demonstrator and didn't like contact with students, and it showed...' was not likely to lead to a full and frank exchange of views on future career prospects.

Many 1986 qualifiers, like their predecessors, got their careers advice informally, often on the job. This advice was mixed and patchy. Respondents voiced their concern about the wisdom of admitting doubts or worries about future careers to any member of staff, since it was generally perceived that this would be regarded as a sign of weakness. There was almost no discussion or advice on such important options as part-time training or part-time career posts in medicine, in spite of the fact that so many of the women were likely to work less than full-time at some point in their careers, and women accounted for around half the students in many of the medical schools at the time.

We found examples of encouraging role models at medical school, but, as we found in the first study, there were more examples of discouraging role models. These were to be found among surgeons in particular, and it must be a matter of concern that an even higher proportion of men and women in my last study than we found among the 1981 qualifiers said that they had been discouraged from surgery at medical school.

There was no evidence that the 1986 qualifiers were any less motivated and determined than any of their predecessors had been. However, what was clear was that they were perhaps more willing to express their discontent with a medical school system which apparently paid such little attention to the pastoral care of its students. The almost complete lack of evidence of a tutorial system which even approached the level found in most other university disciplines over the last fifty years was one of the marked features of these studies on doctors' careers. And yet medical students, particularly in their clinical years, were being exposed to stresses of a much greater magnitude and complexity than any likely to be encountered by students in other fields. We have observed before, like other commentators, that teaching by 'humiliation' appears to be relatively common in medical schools. This is not conducive to reducing stress and enabling medical students to make well-informed and positive decisions about their future careers.

There were signs that women were more diffident than men at medical school about their future prospects, and the quotes from women in my latest report expressing concern that they were not clever enough to do hospital medicine, their feelings of insecurity in the face of their treatment by consultants, and their lack of confidence in their abilities are real indictments of a system which does not recognise or develop the talents of such intelligent young women.

There was a steady increase in the proportion of respondents over the years who thought that women were treated differently from men at medical school, and, although we heard fewer accounts of straight-forward sexist remarks and blatant discrimination, it was still apparently commonplace for women medical students to be subjected to comments from staff which could only have been interpreted as discriminatory under the legislation. Many of the men also found this type of behaviour intolerable. It does seem wrong that so many exceptionally well-qualified young women were left feeling undermined by their treatment at medical school.

The 1986 qualifiers agreed with the strong recommendation given in my first report by qualifiers from all cohorts that there was a need for a more sensitive, systematic and focused approach to the personal and career needs of medical students.

Life in the postgraduate years

The 1986 qualifiers were more likely than their predecessors to have had some idea of what specialty they wished to pursue at entry to medical school. Many of these had changed their minds by the time they qualified, but again the 1986 qualifiers were more likely than their predecessors to have had a specific career intention at qualification. Again, a relatively high proportion changed their minds in the pre-registration year, but fewer of the 1986 qualifiers were opting for general practice at registration than we had found among the 1981 qualifiers at that stage.

The pre-registration year had not been a happy experience for many doctors, with special criticism reserved for house jobs in teaching hospitals. The 1986 qualifiers were more articulate than any other cohort about their dislike at all stages of their careers of being undervalued. The descriptions of the experience of doctors in pre-registration jobs in teaching hospitals – 'treated like clerks' or 'little ants at the bottom of the heap' or 'underdogs', in an atmosphere characterised by 'back-stabbing' and 'boot-licking', were not unusual. I must reiterate that it is probable that young doctors are less and less willing to accept a culture in which such a hierarchical structure is acceptable.

By the time we interviewed them four years after registration, only 60 per cent of the men and less than half the women were still in the same specialty they had chosen at registration. This highlights the danger of making assumptions about career intentions or changes from early statements of intent. Doctors' careers do not usually follow a neat pattern, and specialty intentions even at registration may not always be a real guide to what actually happens. Medical manpower planning has to take into account many other factors which may affect the careers of doctors. One of the most important factors in present-day terms is the extent to which women are likely to want to work less than full-time at some point in their careers. Since women now account for half those entering the medical profession, this is perhaps more important than statements about career or specialty intention at registration or any other time.

However, there is little doubt that early career decisions speed up career progression, and that those who had decided on a specialty at registration, and stuck to it, had made faster progress up the career ladder than those who had not. The perceived stress on progress linked to age and grade remains a formidable force in medicine, and, with the implementation of the Calman Report[4], it appears likely that there may be even less room for manoeuvre.

All this underlines the importance of good careers advice, information and counselling which has been a recurrent theme in these reports. It is as important at the postgraduate stage as at medical school, and it remains important throughout postgraduate training. 1986 qualifiers who had found it difficult to settle on a specialty at an early stage of their careers appeared to be finding it more difficult than others to get satisfactory posts.

And yet, in spite of the undoubted discontent felt by many 1986 qualifiers, both at the time of the interview and in the immediate postgraduate years, less than a handful had left medicine. Some were between jobs, some were deciding what to do, some were studying, but only a tiny number were taking time out to bring up children. Doctors in this country are mostly working, and very few are lost to medicine forever. But perhaps half the women are likely to be working less than full-time, particularly in their thirties. The most important point is to ensure that those who are working are satisfied and secure in their work so that their contribution can be maximised. This means that part-time or less than full-time working must be accorded the same status as full-time working.

How do people choose specialties?

Career choice at entry to medical school is often based on specialties that 18-year-olds know something about – like general practice – or on television programmes – like surgery – or on a vague notion of wanting to work with children – hence paediatrics. Otherwise we found that few doctors had much idea of what specialties were available, let alone any idea of what they might do.

But one of the most interesting things about medicine is that it is a very broad church and that it can offer such an enormously wide range of careers under one generic umbrella. We found that it catered for all kinds of personalities and desires, but somehow many doctors only stumbled across this fact quite late in their careers. One of the most striking findings in all the research I have done is the extent to which, even at the end of medical school, many doctors seem to have had only minimal exposure to certain specialties. I am not talking only about the more exotic sub-specialties but also specialties like radiology, radiotherapy, accident and emergency, public health, geriatric medicine, genitourinary medicine and so on. These were rarely among the choices of doctors at qualification, and more important perhaps, at registration. Why do doctors know so little about them and what could or should be done about it?

I would like to look a little more closely at why people choose certain specialties, and then change their minds again and again in many cases. The range of specialty choice is so varied that one would have thought something could have been found for most people. Some doctors in all my studies have acknowledged this quite freely, like anaesthetists – 'I prefer my patients to be asleep...', 'You have a feeling of satisfaction in putting a patient to sleep and seeing them wake up again...'

Some people preferred no patients at all, like a pathologist: 'My immaturity made it difficult to relate with the clinical side – that is patients. Medicine was OK except for the people...' Another pathologist: 'I became aware that I couldn't really see myself as a clinician. I'm not that kind of person. I'd wanted to be, but I found the whole thing of having to look after people too difficult. I didn't care enough and I wasn't confident enough. I felt I couldn't do them any good – and I didn't give a damn anyway. I had a problem being responsible for myself, let alone other people...'

Women had often wanted to do obstetrics and gynaecology, even if they were to change their minds later: 'I felt that women doctors had a part to play in a situation where women were patients. I thought there was a need for female doctors in this specialty. It was certainly male dominated...' She became a consultant radiologist.

Surgeons often liked their jobs. A 1966 qualifier: 'It struck me as the most successful specialty I saw in making people better quickly. I was also attracted by its demand for quick decision-making...' A young surgical registrar among the 1986 cohort: 'I thoroughly enjoyed surgical practice. There were so many aspects I enjoyed, for example, manual dexterity, the creative side, a lot of young patients, it's instantly gratifying. People came in, had the operation and went out...'

But, as we have seen, not everyone liked surgery – or surgeons. A woman psychiatric registrar in the last study noted the views of one: 'He said women shouldn't be surgeons. They should do things where they can't *kill* people – like family planning...' Surgeons certainly appeared to engender strong emotions in other doctors, and something seems to happen to them when faced with medical students which brings out their least attractive characteristics.

What about psychiatry? Again we came across total misconceptions about what the specialty was all about. There were two young women who had wanted to do psychiatry when they had started at medical school. Perhaps it was just as well they had changed their minds. One had changed to haematology. She said: 'Having done sessions in psychiatry I disliked it intensely. Patients were stressful to look after...'. Another was clearly ill-suited to the specialty, although it seemed to have taken her a while to find out: 'My perception of psychiatry was totally different when I left from when I started. I didn't realise how much other people irritated me. Some drove me crazy and I wanted to slap their faces and say, "Pull yourself together!"'

But for others, it was simply the conditions of work in hospital medicine, the grind, the long hours, the constant moves that I have referred to. A woman had changed to general practice: 'I was disillusioned with hospital medicine. The hours were grim – and the way you were treated – total lack of respect – not even any clean bed-linen when you were on call. My on-call room wasn't cleaned for six months. I slept in the labour ward most of the time...'

And it was this that we returned to time and again. Some of the interviews in this latest study can only be described as heartbreaking. These were the brightest and best of their generation, but by the time we interviewed them we were hearing some very sad tales from people in their late twenties, a time when the world should have been their oyster.

Is this really the way to treat young people? I think that when you hear comments like: 'It's knocked every bit of enthusiasm right out of me. I'm at a massive crisis point – a great big crossroads. I feel I'd like to give up, but I don't know any other trade, so I'm a bit stuck really...' or 'I will always regret becoming a doctor. Ten years of my life would have been better doing something else...' – I feel that there is a real challenge for everyone with any responsibility for the medical profession to do something about a structure which grinds young people down in such an extraordinary way.

References

1   Allen, I. 1994 *Doctors and their Careers: a New Generation* London: Policy Studies Institute

2   Allen, I. 1988 *Doctors and their Careers* London: Policy Studies Institute

3   Allen, I. 1988 *Any Room at the Top?* London: Policy Studies Institute

4   Department of Health 1993 *Hospital Doctors: Training for the Future. The Report of the Working Group on Specialist Medical Training* (The Calman Report), Department of Health

Discussion from the floor

The discussion of this paper was taken after Robert Hale's paper (page 36).

HOW PATIENTS MAKE THEIR DOCTORS ILL

Robert Hale

My theme is that not only do doctors have to learn to adapt to a demanding and even difficult profession, but that we must offer those working within the medical system an environment which will allow them to work effectively, and to survive and even enjoy their work. Medicine has some inevitable stresses; others are not inevitable, and we should be alert to ways in which we can reduce stress not just for young doctors but for all of us.

The Tavistock Clinic offers a service to which doctors can refer themselves for psychological help. I think it is important to refer to it as *psychological help* and not to call the doctors *sick doctors* because that jump of calling yourself sick is an important hurdle which many people are reluctant to make. In consequence some do not seek help until too late. I want to try and point out the ways in which things go wrong and right for doctors as revealed by some of the accounts that my patients give me. I see about thirty doctors a year, a relatively small number, for consultation, and then they stay in psychotherapy with me for up to a couple of years.

I have brought some illustrative clinical material from a Saturday morning session with a doctor. She has given me permission to use this.

> *Elegant Sarah is apparently the epitome of a successful young doctor. She comes from an academic family and despite rebellious teens she managed by the time she was 18 to have a choice between medical school and music school. By her mid-twenties she had achieved exceptional academic results and was established in a golden circuit medical registrar job.*

Sarah begins by saying that after the previous session she had realised how hard a time she was giving her boyfriend. She had apologised but he had thrown it back in her face. The therapist observes that she is fed up that the therapy seems to make things more difficult by stirring up feelings that make trouble for her.

Sarah: 'Well it's been a pretty lousy fortnight. My boss has been away, there has been this terribly sick woman, we thought she was going to die. The awful thing was we could not find out why. We just had to watch her going downhill. The other consultants came and gave their opinions but they didn't really seem concerned the way my boss does. She had septicaemia and we couldn't find the cause. It was all very well for those other consultants – she wasn't their patient. They could just walk away from her. On my nights off I just couldn't sleep.'

She then returns to the theme of the previous session in which she felt that in some ways she was a princess who could get what she wants and can get people to do what she wants. She begins to cry.

Sarah: 'You are just not expected to be weak when you are a doctor. The day before yesterday I was caught in the corridor by the wife of a man who has leukaemia. The consultant was going to tell him at lunchtime but his wife had already guessed. She was furious with me and I couldn't tell her. I had been up all the night before and I really couldn't cope with her shouting at me. I didn't handle it at all well. I went to the sluice and locked the door and cried for a bit.'

The therapist reminded Sarah that she had rung the previous week to say that she could not make the session because she was still coping with the patients she had admitted from the night before. He suggested that as a patient with him she must somewhere feel that he should make time for her in the way she makes time for her patients.

Sarah: 'Yes, but look what it does to you when you really care about your patients. My boss, Brian, he has been a consultant for only two years. He is 39, he looks twenty years older. He is the one that everyone wants to refer patients to because he cares. He works morning, noon and night.'

The therapist said she sounded worried about who looked after Brian and that she perhaps felt responsible for him.

Sarah: 'Well, I don't want to look after him and I am not sure now that I want to be him. The other day I found myself sitting in the middle of the ward saying out loud, "Where am I going?" and people said, "now Sarah is really losing her marbles."*

Therapist: 'How do you cope without losing your marbles?'.*

Sarah: 'Well, most medics do. They can just shut off. They can look at it as an intellectual exercise. Even Brian does that at times. We had a post-mortem over the woman that just died. We all sat round and talked about the pathological findings. Nobody really talked about what they felt inside.'*

Therapist: 'I think you are struggling to find a place where you can talk about these feelings and in a way I think that you have to bring that feeling function for the whole of your unit to this session.'*

Sarah: 'Yes, but that's not much use because how can I feed it back into them when they can't hear it.'*

This clinical material is brief but it concentrates many of the issues which young doctors do have to face and it illustrates some of the 'normal' anxieties of being a doctor. There are anxieties that are peculiar to medicine and the practice of medicine, and I believe we build individual and institutional defences against these anxieties.

For the most part these defences serve us well and they allow us to work. Sometimes however they fail. On the one hand the defensive structure may become excessive and the doctor becomes the over-intellectual but coping doctor; on the other hand all the defences may fail, and the doctor becomes ill, either psychologically or physically.

What are the anxieties specifically facing people working in medicine? I have practised medicine in three settings, the general hospital, the psychiatric hospital and the forensic setting and I think that anxieties seen in all three can be observed in general practice.

There are three fundamental anxieties that have to be faced. In the general hospital it is the anxiety and the sadness of disease and dying. In the psychiatric hospital there is the anxiety and even the fear of madness, of falling apart psychically. And in the forensic setting it is the fear of corruption, that we are being taken for a ride, or being coerced. All three of those overlap and all three will be recognised by the general physician working in general practice.

Anxieties of doctors

Let us look at medical anxieties in general, the anxieties of doctors working in the general hospital.

There is first the anxiety of dealing with age and decrepitude. For young people dealing with the elderly is sometimes quite a painful experience because it reminds us of our mortality, but even as we get older ourselves, anxiety about ageing may not get less, and may even increase.

There is the anxiety of death and the process of dying, which are not the same. Something junior doctors most dread is breaking bad news to relatives. As a junior doctor I hoped that the terminally ill patient died when I wasn't on call so that someone else would have to tell the relatives.

There is the anxiety of observing pain, whether it be physical or psychical.

There is the anxiety of being impotent, of facing disease and being able to do little about it. A doctor who can see the well patient walk out of hospital is fortunate and in those specialties where many people do not get better it is hard for people to cope. Psychiatry for example is hard for doctors because our patients do not get better in that very dramatic way.

The last anxiety that I would name is disgust. It is not much talked about but I suspect that sometimes patients and their disorders present us with things which actually are quite repellent. I think that we require doctors to transform the unacceptable into the mundane on a daily basis. For some patients there is an element of shame in their physical and psychical problems which arouse sympathy alongside disgust. In others the patient may expect the doctor to accept anything he may bring. As a forensic psychiatrist working with sexual criminals I am daily bombarded with things which make me feel both physically and morally disgusted yet my patients expect me to be able to cope with that.

Doctors' defences

Not all defences are maladaptive; clearly we must have coping strategies to work effectively but some of the ways we use to cope with stress can be harmful to ourselves, our patients and our colleagues and families.

Firstly we *deny* we are experiencing any anxiety, any tension within ourselves. This is the defence of hypomania in which we become workaholics. I call it riding the tiger, from the saying 'he who rides the tiger dare not dismount'. The new deal has reduced the hours that doctors work, and that can only be in large measure a good thing. However, in a recent survey Liam Hudson and I found that SHOs experiencing the greatest stress were the ones working the least hours. There was an inverse relationship between hours of work and stress experienced, perhaps because if you stop you have to face all of the pain.

Altruism may seem a strange defence because many of us go in to medicine largely out of altruistic motives, yet altruism can be a defence against conflict and anxiety.

Intellectualisation, or I would call it medicalisation, is ubiquitous. We often talk about the liver or the biochemical medical problem and ignore what the patient is actually experiencing.

It may seem strange to nominate *hypochondria* as a defence but I think it is part of the defensive structure that we actually take on the illnesses that our patients have. I do not know of a medical student who has not had Hodgkin's disease or leukaemia. Of course we always choose the illnesses which are fatal, no one ever becomes hypochondriacal about eczema. We select fatal diseases because in surviving them we reduce anxiety.

Eroticization, is again perhaps familiar to some and not to others. We may see this in for example the over-familiarity of the operating theatre. This is the stuff that television soaps are made of. Look at the advance notice of *Casualty* or *ER*. The theme of sexual titillation is often there and I do not think that is any coincidence. It is a way that we cope and is a way of reminding ourselves in some way that we are alive, vibrant and active sexually. In this way sexual excitement may help us avoid the pain of what we are dealing with in our patients.

And lastly, *'acting out'*. 'Acting out' suggests an action which helps avoid something which is painful to feel, though the action itself may be harmful. We go out and get pissed with our mates: medical students are very good at that. We also commit suicide, and sadly doctors have enormously high suicide rates. Another way of acting out is to become medically overactive. Generally this is giving an unnecessary prescription, but I have heard doctor patients say that they could not cope with the anxiety of not operating so they cut open the patient's abdomen. This need actually to *do* something runs through medicine.

What determines the doctor–patient relationship

I would like to suggest that it is the patients and their needs who dictate the design of the system. Think of a court of law and who is in it. There is a prosecutor, a defence lawyer, a judge, a jury, probation officer, social worker, gaoler, and the public outside. Now each of them performs a function which the criminal needs performed for him. In other words, they represent part of his inner world. He needs someone who is a judge, someone who will prosecute him, someone who will defend him, someone who will punish him, someone who will be impartial and so on. So that the external organisation of the court of law may parallel and enact the inner theatre of his mind.

So too in hospitals, I think that the patients create the hospital around them. The various conscious and unconscious needs of the patients seek a relationship with different people and parts of the organisation. To a large extent, the roles within the organisation thus develop to meet the needs of the patients. Thus senior doctors, junior doctors, nurses, occupational therapists and so on, in a way are representatives of the inner world of the patient. We act as spokespersons for the unconscious self of the patient and fulfil the roles that our patients or our clients point us to.

We have to find out and allow doctors to ask the question: what sort of a doctor am I? In other words, what are my internal structures and how do they relate to the outside world? Some doctors do it better than others. Some do it too well and become the uncritical acolytes of the system, and so nothing changes, and so getting the balance between someone who will accept the system and someone who will kick against the system is crucial.

Institutions and their defences

I would thoroughly recommend a book called *Social Systems as a Defence Against Anxiety* by Isabel Menzies Lyth. It is work from the 1950s and 1960s but rings true now. Menzies Lyth looks at the way in which the organisational structure in hospitals may defend individuals from anxiety. She examines the hospital routines and rituals which can develop to help staff avoid the anxieties of their work, and details the difficulties this may create for individuals working within the system.

When an individual's defences fail they become ill. When an institution's defences fail that institution becomes ill. A prison medical officer said to me recently, 'My job is to look after the health of the prison. If I have got a healthy prison I have got healthy prisoners'.

Within the health service we assume that the structure, healthy or otherwise, is created and maintained by administrators and by other senior staff including consultants.

Living with Health Service changes

Hospitals grew out of religious institutions, which represents the altruism and the philanthropy central to the practice of medicine, and we cannot ignore the fact of the recent changes in the health service. These changes have introduced a new set of values which may or may not be necessary. My experience with many of the doctors whom I see as patients is that the new values can be felt to be contradictory to these original more altruistic values.

About a third of the doctors whom I saw last year came to me as a result of the changes in the health service and their inability to cope. Among this group troubled by the changes there were more consultants than junior doctors. Sometimes when the patient was a junior doctor I had the sense that the junior doctor was the emissary of the firm. On one occasion, a firm was going through a particularly difficult time in meeting its targets and its junior doctor, who was taking the stick for the problems, broke down and came to treatment. I contend that the new ways of the health service may undermine the existing defensive structures which doctors have built up, both at a personal level and again at an institutional level.

Conclusion

What will life be like for the doctors of tomorrow? Doctors have to adapt to a changing world and changing practice of medicine. We have to accept that a capacity to change and adapt to different systems is an important part of being a doctor: the doctors of today have to be different from the doctors of ten years ago and will have to be different again ten years hence.

Yet the systems must also support those who work within them. We have a responsibility not only to choose tomorrow's doctors but also to create a system which allows them to learn and practise the sort of medicine that they, and I think we, firmly believe in.

Discussion from the floor

The point was made that whilst we must acknowledge that some doctors suffer problems and that we should be aware of this, we should also remember that many doctors enjoy their work, are very competent, and get great satisfaction from being a doctor. Another participant thought that most doctors like their work but do not like the conditions they now have to work under.

Robert Hale responded that he was trying to emphasise that even in the successful doctor there are tensions and anxieties which each of us has to deal with, but that we should also remember that there are some 'non-successes' in medicine, and there are large areas of medicine which are traps for non-success. He reminded the audience that those present were probably representative of success and that we, the successful ones, are the ones that set the rules, we are the examiners, we are the tutors, we are the seniors in medicine.

A participant remarked that some students choose science subjects because they want to do medicine and do not only choose medicine because they are good at science.

Isobel Allen emphasised that many of the things that women do not like about the medical career structure are what men do not like as well. There are changes in society as a whole and people are not as prepared to put up with certain things as they were before. Medicine itself has changed and although older consultants had perhaps worked longer hours when they were junior doctors, they were less isolated and had to work less intensively when on call.

A mature student had found that being older, he was much more motivated, and had built up a much better support structure. He queried whether medicine might be improved by becoming a graduate-only entry course.

It was noted that people who studied other subjects and changed to something were not usually described as having failed in their first field of study. However, in medicine there seemed to be a taboo about being a 'failed medic'.

DOES MATURITY MAKE A DIFFERENCE?

Tessa Blackstone

Introduction

There is a simple answer to the question, 'does maturity make a differ-ence?'. It is yes, it certainly does make a difference. And it makes a difference for the better. I will expand on this, drawing on my experi-ence of running Birkbeck College.

Birkbeck is Britain's leading higher education institution for the education of mature part-time students. It now caters for some 5,600 students studying for postgraduate and undergraduate degrees and there are another 22,000 working all over London who are doing extra-mural courses, which are even more part-time and are for certifi-cates or diplomas. We cover a wide range of subjects: pure science, many arts subjects and most of the social sciences. And it is an institu-tion that has grown very rapidly in recent years. So I think it demonstrates that there is a demand from mature students to study at degree level.

One of the things that I have become aware of in my time at Birkbeck is that mature students are particularly interested in vocational courses that will lead them into a profession of one kind or another. That does not mean to say that there are not many mature students who want to study for the sake of studying and come and do a degree in something like philosophy, but certainly in the new depart-ments of Management and Business Studies and of Law we have a huge surplus of applicants over places.

The characteristics of mature students

High motivation

What characterises mature students? What are their special qualities? First of all they have a passionate commitment to study. They are very highly motivated and it isn't really surprising that they are highly motivated because they are making considerable sacrifices to study. They are giving up sometimes quite well-paid jobs to come back into full-time education or they are studying part-time, and giving up leisure time and time with their families.

Certainty about study and career choice

In most cases mature students have a degree of certainty about their choice of subject which younger students often lack. The reason for this, I think, is fairly obvious: they have thought about it a great deal. Quite often they have studied something else before and discovered, unfortunately, *en route* that they did not make quite the right choice the first time round. So they are usually very determined the second time round to make the right choice, and they do give it a great deal of thought before finally making a decision.

A dedicated approach to learning

Mature students have a very conscientious and dedicated approach to learning. They are there because they have thought through the decision to study rather than simply being on the escalator: younger students have come through the sixth form, they have done well, and the escalator almost automatically will take them these days into higher education, often without a lot of consideration about what is entailed.

High standards

They tend to have a very self-critical approach to their own work as students. They are very conscious of what it is to attain a high standard, and if they do not reach those high standards, they are critical about their own performance. Related to this and in a sense perhaps as a consequence of it they sometimes lack confidence about what they are doing. And this is especially true of those students who are returning after a very long gap between their school experiences and coming back into higher education. Of course, a lack of confidence can also be destructive, and people who teach mature students have to build confidence in their students' ability.

Breadth of experience

Mature students have considerable ability to place what they are learning in a rather broader context. They are able, of course, to draw on their own experience of life in a way that an 18-year-old student will find rather more difficult. I am not saying that 18-year-old students cannot do this – everything that I am saying is about relative rather than absolute differences. Associated with this ability to look beyond what they are studying and place it in a broader context is a very questioning, critical approach to the teaching that they get. They will not just sit and listen. You cannot as a teacher of mature students simply didactically drop the pearls of wisdom and expect them to be picked up. They will challenge those who teach them.

Gratitude and loyalty

Lastly, mature students have a genuine gratitude for what is for many a second chance for higher education. People who miss out earlier can often become very dejected and have a rather poor self-image about themselves relative to their peers. Coming back can be of enormous importance in terms of rebuilding their self-image. I sometimes get moving letters from students who have been accepted to study at Birkbeck, saying that for all their lives they have deeply regretted the fact that they did not go to university, they thought they would never be able to, and they thank the College for giving them what they see as a wonderful opportunity and a second chance. I frequently meet former graduates of the College in my travels round the country who say that coming to Birkbeck changed their lives. I do not think that this has much to do with Birkbeck – you would find the same gratitude towards their medical school from mature students of medicine.

Teaching mature students

My own staff's attitude to teaching mature students is enormously positive. Those who come to Birkbeck, having taught in other universities, often comment on what they like most about being in the institution: this is not their colleagues; it is not that they are now in a five-rated research department compared with a lower rated one before; it is not the fact that the scientific equipment that is available is better than what they had before. What they most enjoy is the challenge of teaching mature students. It is a very enjoyable experience because they test you, they push you, they teach each other and they teach you. I have never come across anybody working with adult students who doesn't say that there are frequently occasions when they learn from their students. There is an atmosphere of mutual support among students who are studying the tough way when they are older. All my staff also comment on the wonderful diversity you get in a class of mature students. At Birkbeck we have students who come from a remarkable range of different backgrounds in terms of their educational experience, and people who are doing or have done an enormous range of jobs: from actresses to deep sea divers, from bank clerks to merchant bankers.

The demand from mature students

There are people who might think that the great increase in opportunities for higher education at school-leaving age will mean that there is no longer going to be a demand from older students (after all, 30 per cent of young people leaving school can go to a university somewhere or other). I very much doubt that. As the number in higher education has expanded so has the number of mature students. Indeed the expansion of demand from older people has been much greater than it has been from school-leavers. Between 1987 and 1992 applications from those over 21 years of age rose by 215 per cent; applications from those under 21 rose by 66 per cent. About a quarter of applicants in 1992 were over 21, about 12.5 per cent applicants in the same year were over 25, and since then the trend has been towards further growth. There has been an increase of 262 per cent in mature students in the system as a whole since 1987. Over half of all those actually studying today are over 21. Both social and economic change is contributing to this. People get married much later than they did. The gap between marriage and starting a family is now much longer than it used to be. The average age of having a first child amongst women in this country is now 28. If that is the average then it is going to be quite a lot higher for highly educated graduate women.

Education can obviously be continued much more easily into your late twenties and early thirties if you do not yet have a family to look after. In the past, what tended to happen was that education came first; its end was a kind of catalyst for marriage, followed swiftly by having children. Secondly, far fewer people are committed early to a job for life in a single organisation. There are fewer people who have a simple straightforward 'throughout-life career' today. There is far more switching of careers, much more uncertainty and insecurity in the labour market and, of course, there is more unemployment. Therefore there are a lot of people deciding to start to study in a new field as adults in their mid- to late twenties and thirties. Thirdly, the development of continuing education and of life-long education (it is in fact the European Year of Life-Long Education this year) is clearly having an impact. In other words it is catching: studying amongst people in their late twenties, thirties and even older is no longer perceived as a rather strange aberration or eccentric behaviour. If you have friends who have decided to go to university later in life you might think about doing it yourself.

Another factor is marital breakdown and divorce. Just as people may leave their careers and start again, people who leave their marriages also look for change in their lives outside the domestic sphere. One route to make such changes is to start a university course. The end of a relationship is, in fact, sometimes cited as a reason for coming back into higher education, and some students appear to do so partly in the hope of finding a new partner!

What is clear is that a job for life, a career for life, a husband or wife for life, can no longer be assumed. There are discontinuities both at home and at work. Our lives have a much more episodic character, and this will continue and will propel more adult students back into post-school education of different kinds.

Mature students in medicine

An under-represented group
Where does all this leave medicine? Circumstantial evidence tells me that there are a much smaller proportion in medicine than there are in most other subjects. Anecdotal evidence also tells me that there are still considerable difficulties experienced by older people trying to get in to medical schools. I will just give you one little example. The daughter of a friend of mine who recently graduated in biological sciences – a degree in which she had done two papers in biochemistry – was forced to take chemistry A-level before a medical school would admit her. Frankly, this seems to me utterly absurd.

The cost-benefit of mature medical students
Are there any arguments against having more mature students in medical schools? I think there is really only one: that it is an expensive and long training. It is a big investment from the individual's point of view and from society's point of view, and the number of years in which medical graduates contribute to the system by working as practitioners should be as great as possible. But there are many other expensive and long courses around today. It is an expensive and long course to train as an architect and I do not believe schools of architecture are as difficult about letting in older students as medical schools. It takes a long time to train a research scientist, seven years minimum,

where I suspect there are far more mature students. However, whilst there is scope for medical schools to relax a bit about this, I am willing to accept that the usual thing that I say when talking to people about being a mature student – 'it is never too old to start' – may not entirely apply to medicine. There is probably a point when you are too old to start because of the considerable cost involved. However, to get 25 to 30 years out of somebody, which should be the case for those completing a medical course between the ages of 30 and 40, seems acceptable.

Maturity and medical practice

Dare I suggest that some of those who start later may even be better doctors? Their greater maturity may make them more skilled as communicators, may make them more sensitive to their patients' concerns and it certainly may make them better able to cope with some of the stresses of being a doctor today. These were the arguments I used, incidentally, when talking to the law profession about the setting up of a law degree at Birkbeck, and they were accepted by senior people in the Bar and in the Law Society. Also, people who have done other things first may bring things into medicine which are valuable.

Conclusion

Should we not go out of our way to encourage more mature students to study medicine? Moreover, ought we not even to consider whether a slightly faster track through may be possible for mature students? There is a lot to be learnt as a medical student but younger students of all kinds do spend a certain amount of their day devoted to play. Mature students do not need to spend their time on play, they have done their play earlier in life and they want to get on. I wonder whether at least at the pre-clinical stage and possibly at the clinical stage they might go a little faster.

Let me conclude with a suggestion for St George's, who are hosting this conference, and will soon be the only free-standing medical school in the country. It could be the institution that has a special commitment to taking mature students, as they do not really need to mix with students in other subjects in quite the same way as younger students – again, they have done their mixing as they have done their playing. If medicine in general, and St George's in particular, took that route you would have many wonderful students who would bring a great deal to their studies and to their practice later.

Discussion from the floor

Sir William Asscher, the Principal of St George's Hospital Medical School responded to Tessa Blackstone's suggestion by agreeing that there ought to be more mature students in medicine, and noting that the School already practised a policy of welcoming them: approximately 10 per cent of the intake were mature students, some of them in their early thirties. A policy of encouraging applicants to take a gap year between school and medical school was also being followed. It was important, he noted, to achieve the right mix of school leavers and mature students.

Two mature medical students contributed with comments supporting the general characterisations offered by Tessa Blackstone. However, they also pointed out the considerable barriers which mature students come up against: they had experienced a lack of flexibility, both of entry requirements and of course structure, particularly for those who have children. There was a call for medical schools to find ways in which mature entrants could be given more credit for what they had done in a first degree in a related subject. The greatest concern was about financial barriers, especially recent increases in self-financing fee levels which some schools had implemented or were considering. Such increases, it was suggested, should be opposed strongly.

It was pointed out that the maintenance element of support was the greatest financial barrier to mature students. Local authorities now increasingly would not exercise the discretion to pay for students to do a second degree. The whole question of discretionary fees for mature students with an existing degree was something for political parties and the government to look at. Tessa Blackstone noted that the whole system of financing students was likely to be changed whatever government is in power. One reason for changing was the absurd situation in which local authorities were left to make decisions about discretionary awards, without enough money to support discretionary students, and with all sorts of quite bizarre distinctions between what qualified for a discretionary award and what did not. She did not believe that the current system of maintenance grants was going to survive, and that we were likely to have a system based on loans or maintenance grants repaid on an income contingent basis later. This, she thought, should help mature students because they ought to be eligible for loans and be able to repay them later just as all other students could.

The question was raised of how prevalent attitudes towards mature students could be changed. Tessa Blackstone considered that this had to be done in two ways: firstly by people within institutions fighting for a more progressive approach; secondly by finding incentives for medical schools at a national level.

ETHICAL ISSUES IN THE SELECTION OF MEDICAL STUDENTS

Joe Collier

It is important to recognise that there is a special relationship between medical education and society at large. There are three reasons for this. First, in the UK medical education is funded by the community through monies raised by general taxation. Second, medical education is geared to produce doctors who can cater for the public's health needs. In keeping with this, the number of students selected for medical education in the UK is ultimately determined by staffing requirements of the National Health Service (NHS). Finally, once qualified and in service, the majority of UK doctors work in the public sector. All these features give the ethics of medical student selection a unique dimension since ethical issues themselves are also intimately linked with society and its values.

Definitions and their implications

In this talk I will use 'working' definitions based on the views expressed by Kant. I have chosen his position because it has determined much of my own conduct. Ethics is the study of morals. Morals can be defined as rules of good and bad conduct and in particular the way people should treat each other.

Kant held that an act is morally good if it has as its intended outcome the good of humanity or society as a whole. Accordingly, an over-riding moral principle is that one should act out of respect for others. One consequence of this position is that an act cannot be morally good if it results in people being used as a means to an end. Accordingly any arrangement whereby the success of one group is achieved at the expense of, and by implication is a disadvantage to, another is immoral.

46

These positions can be developed to cover everyday behaviour. Being *honest* to others is morally good; essentially people have a right not to be deceived. While there are circumstances where one might wish to deceive, in principle the starting position must be an obligation to conduct relationships on a basis of honesty. *Transparency* is clearly a component of honesty. The derivation and implementation of policies should be transparent and explicit: the public has a right to know. Nonetheless any system should allow confidentiality to be honoured for those personal matters that have no institutional bearing. The notion of equality also follows from Kant's position; individuals have a right to *equality of treatment*.

Inevitably these rights (to honesty, transparency and equality) will themselves usher in conflicts. Honesty could do harm, transparency may undermine the chances of achieving a legitimate final goal, can there be equality when people have such very different characteristics? However, in the context of student selection, and so institutional (public) rather than personal issues, honesty, transparency and equality must prevail.

The notion of equality of treatment also needs pursuing. Conduct should not discriminate against people unfairly, and one component of that conduct is to treat people so that they are not unfairly barred from achieving the same goals or expectations. The 'goals' concept can be illustrated using an analogy of analgesia for patients in pain. A doctor confronted by patients with varying levels of pain could treat all of them equally by giving all of them the same dose of the same analgesic, say paracetamol. This option, although it offers equality at one level, is clearly unreasonable. The goals-based approach offers a more equitable approach. Here the doctor might choose a goal of say, a pain-free state, and then prescribe whatever analgesics were needed to achieve that state. In this instance treatments would be individually tailored and might differ from patient to patient. Using the goal-based (or expectation-based) model, student selection would ensure that schoolchildren from different backgrounds should not be barred unfairly from their goal of entering medical schools, and that after entering medical school, education would be tailored to help each student achieve his or her (legitimate) expectations.

Selection of medical students

From the above there is an ethical imperative that the selection of students should be geared to produce doctors who are competent to staff the NHS, and a medical profession which in all clinical disciplines and at all levels reflects the composition of the UK population (gender, race, class etc) and serves it with equity. There is also a practical requirement that they will be able to teach and undertake research.

Principles of selection

In reality the selection of students expressly to staff the NHS and to serve the needs of the nation as a whole would be very difficult to meet, partly because we do not know what competently serving patients actually implies. In the face of such uncertainty there is a compelling argument for opening up the selection system and with it stating the criteria for selection. Ultimately, whatever mechanism for selection is used, the criteria should incorporate agreed, measurable and realistic specifications; the actual process should be monitored and its immediate and long-term outcomes assessed; and finally the criteria and process should be reviewed and modified to ensure goals are met. In the UK little of this is done, especially at a national level. Some monitoring does occur but on an ad hoc basis. This is reflected by a recent paper from the Commission for Racial Equality which suggests that 'Medical Schools should take legally permissible positive action measures to encourage applications from ethnic minority women – in particular black women ...' (from the CRE's report, *Appointing NHS Consultants and Senior Registrars*, published in May 1996).

The ideals of explicit criteria and monitoring are a long way from being adopted formally. Even where information relating to certain steps in the selection process is collected, data for review are not easy to obtain at either a local or a national level. A vast amount of data are obtained by UCAS but these remain confidential and seemingly unavailable for independent scrutiny.

Who should select medical students?

Transparency and review is only of value if it helps define a crucial issue which is to establish what actually makes a good doctor. With such uncertainty is it appropriate for the medical profession alone to be the judges of future requirements or should there be others involved, such as patients or the wider public? Without them, and representatives of government, medicine is at risk of appointing the next generation of doctors in its own image; of producing a profession that serves itself rather than the public. It is my belief that this has probably been the case for many years. To fulfil the wider ethical criteria members of the public should contribute to the process; it is they after all, who get ill, pay taxes and who can be legitimate representatives of society. Patients can no longer afford to delegate to the medical profession the responsibility for selection, rather selection should be done as part of a partnership. If the public were asked what they wanted of doctors they would probably start with the need for doctors to have a detailed knowledge of illness, diagnosis and treatment, but other criteria may also come high on the list such as an ability to communicate, to listen, to empathise and sympathise, and to have flexibility of mind. It is in order to involve the public that selection criteria must be transparent, and outcomes amenable to more public scrutiny.

Ethics and education at medical school

Ethical issues continue to arise while the student is at medical school; the style and content of education is also subject to ethical constraints. In addition to upholding the rights to equality of treatment, honesty and transparency, it is again important that society at large is involved in helping determine the content of the course. In my view courses and contents, themes and goals, should be open to scrutiny by the public (and patients) working in partnership with the profession; it should certainly not be left to doctors alone to oversee the curriculum and its implementation, yet often this is still being done. A far reaching review of medical education in the UK, coupled with recommendations on change, has recently been published by the General Medical Council (GMC, *Tomorrow's Doctors*, 1993). Of the twelve members on the working party responsible for the report none was a representative of an ethnic minority and only one was a woman. Moreover when the group gathered evidence and sought opinion, which involved visits to the medical schools and repeated circulation of drafts for comment, relatively little time was devoted to formally seeking the views of the public or patients. To me the omission of these wider views was unethical. It certainly does not sit easily with the GMC's own mission 'statement' – 'Protecting Patients, Guiding Doctors'.

Selection continues after the student qualifies

Selection does not stop on entry to medical school. At every exam during both medical training and after graduation, and at every job interview, choices will be made which will determine the career of the candidate. Ultimately, they will also determine the composition and character of the medical profession. That being so, the general ethical principles outlined earlier, such as transparency, equality of treatment and the involvement of the public, should be applied as an integral part of each selection process. Job interviews and exams, be they final MBBS, MRCP, MRCGP, FRCS or whatever, should incorporate issues defined as important to the public, such as communication skills, and should take place with the full involvement of consumer/patient representatives. The failure of the Royal Colleges to involve the public in their arrangements for higher professional exams needs review. To its credit, the Royal College of General Practitioners now makes an 'Assessment of competence in consulting skills' part of its MRCGP exam. In the assessment candidates submit videos of consultations in order to allow their consulting skills to be judged. Using the videos, examiners assess whether the candidates can elicit the patient's account of his or her symptoms; elicit information about the patient's social, psychological and occupational circumstances, and place the illness in these contexts; and can explore the patient's health understanding. Despite this imaginative development the College still fails to grasp a crucial element in the partnership. Sadly those assessing the skills will all be doctors; surely it would be expedient to involve patients in the process.

Conclusion

I believe that selection to medical school, education and assessments in medical school, and examinations and job interviews after medical school, should all adhere closely to ethical principles. When such adherence occurs, particularly when the composition of the medical profession fully reflects that of society at large, then advantages will flow. I envisage that in the wake of such changes clinical interests will broaden, research interests will become more diverse, patients' interests more readily satisfied, students' interests better addressed and the medical profession more richly endowed and more effective. If this is the product of ethical behaviour, it is difficult to argue against its wholesale adoption.

Discussion from the floor

In discussion, it was noted that if the composition of medical school entry were required to reflect the composition of society as a whole, then we might find that we had to discriminate against better qualified women, in order to allow 50 per cent of students to be men. Positive action should be distinguished from positive discrimination. Positive action would create a training which would allow people from groups which are poorly represented in medicine to train as doctors. Positive discrimination would be unacceptable.

Applicants, it was noted, were overwhelmingly from social classes I-III. More than half still came from independent schools. In one large local comprehensive in a middle class area, there were whole years where no one was considering medicine as a career. Education about being a doctor should start before students applied to medical school; it should begin in school. It could or perhaps should be done in partnership with non-medical people.

Several participants said that we were constrained by the tyranny of A-level results which inevitably led to more candidates from 'academic hothouses'. If we insisted on students taking a year out before applying, this might improve.

A representative of the GMC disputed Joe Collier's claim that the GMC did not consult widely among patient groups.

Worry about money and especially the prospect of beginning a career with large debts was a possible reason that more students from lower socio-economic backgrounds and more mature students do not apply for medicine.

INTRODUCING CHANGE IN THE PROCESS OF SELECTION

John Collins

Introduction

We are celebrating today the Bicentenary of Edward Jenner's first inoculation against smallpox. Jenner was born in 1749 when the patterns of British medical practice and education were undergoing gradual change. Introducing change was a lifelong mission for Jenner as he battled the scourge of smallpox against the criticisms of those who did not share his view. In *Maxims for Revolutionists* George Bernard Shaw wrote: 'the reasonable man adapts himself to the world, the unreasonable one persists in trying to adapt the world to himself, therefore all progress depends on the unreasonable man'.

Perhaps Jenner was such a man and at times medical schools need a Jenner to bring about change or at least encourage Faculty to enter the debate on important controversies. In New Zealand during the 1980s such a debate focused on the process by which our medical students were selected and on the need for this to change.

There are two medical schools in New Zealand, one in Otago and one in Auckland. The Auckland School was founded in 1968 and since then about 3,000 students have entered the course. The annual intake of 115–120 students is made up of 80 school leavers, 25 mature entrants and up to 12 students selected through an affirmative action programme.

Although the process of selection of all entrants has undergone change, this presentation focuses on the largest group, school leavers, where the most significant changes have occurred. Historically these students were selected on the basis of their performance in the national school-leaving examination or on academic criteria alone.

One hundred and thirty applicants were called for interview on the basis of their academic achievement and this interview was mainly a careers guidance and recruitment process, the outcome of which did not alter the ranking set academically. The large number interviewed was to cover for those who might later refuse the offer of a place or wish to defer for one year. The use of academic criteria alone for selection and of a single measurement of it, school leaving marks, became the subject of major controversy and debate. This debate was supported and encouraged by what might be called 'the coming together of a climate for change' which was made up of five separate components.

The climate for change in the selection process

Firstly, the community, both lay and professional, as well as university staff and faculty members were requesting change. Secondly, the experienced admissions committee was aware of existing problems with selection. Thirdly, the rising academic requirements for admission, and fourthly the findings from a prospective study of entrants to the School had to be acknowledged. Finally, the dean was conscious of the concerns of the admissions committee and the community and was supportive of change.

Community, University and Faculty request for change
In 1985 a national conference on the role of the doctor in New Zealand took place which included delegates from the community. One of its recommendations stated that 'qualities other than academic ability should be included and that medical schools be invited to review student selection criteria and procedures and allow community participation in the process.'

The following year a review of the Auckland School of Medicine was undertaken by Auckland University and the ensuing report recorded that: 'concerns were expressed that those selected were not being adequately assessed for communication skills, personality attributes or their involvement in community activities.'

In 1988 the New Zealand Medical Council undertook a review of undergraduate medical education in New Zealand and recommended that 'medical schools be invited to review admission policies with the aim of broadening the effective criteria for selection'. This report also listed six criteria which should be incorporated into the selection of medical students. These included evidence of appropriate communication skills, familiarity with those outside one's community and ethnic group, knowledge of and demonstrable interest in the provision of health care in New Zealand, an understanding of Maori culture and customs, experiences which exposed applicants to a range of different people and situations and finally evidence of academic achievement or potential.

At the same time the community was becoming increasingly vociferous about the poor interpersonal skills of some doctors and the Medical Council Professional Conduct Committee raised concerns about the non-technical aspects of patient care, particularly communication skills, empathy and ethics of practice.

Admissions Committee concerns

Members of the Admissions Committee were concerned about the inevitable margin of error around the cut-off mark in the school-leaving examination required for selection. How does one decide on a 2-mark difference that one applicant is better than another?

The panels involved in interviewing applicants expressed their disquiet about the loss of potential students whom they had perceived at interview to have outstanding personal qualities but who fell below the academic cut-off mark. School principals were disturbed that certain applicants considered by them and their teachers to have ideal personal qualities were excluded on narrow academic marks and that the medical school was sending the wrong message to would-be applicants. In effect there was no encouragement for these young people to become involved in the life of their school, in sport or in the community, rather it was an academic focus alone which was being promoted.

Rising academic requirements for admission

Historically the top academic 10 per cent of New Zealand school leavers were invited for interview but with the increasing competition for places a situation arose where only the top 1-2 per cent of academic achievers were invited or those whose marks were in excess of 82 per cent in the national school-leaving examination. This raises the question of whether it is appropriate to confine selection of students to this group.

Findings from a prospective study

A review of the selection of Auckland medical students over the first 25 years of the school found that one in ten students failed to complete the course and that academic failure and voluntary withdrawal were of equal importance, yet these students were selected on the basis of their academic achievement.[1]

In an attempt to analyse the relationship between the academic requirements for admission and subsequent performance in medical school a longitudinal study was carried out on five cohorts of entrants joining the course directly from secondary school between the years 1982 and 1986. This study of 413 students was completed on the graduation of the 1986 class at the end of 1991. Multiple measurements of their performance throughout the course were made and compared with their school-leaving marks. Such research is difficult due to methodological problems. The narrow range of marks in the school-leaving examinations achieved by those selected has implications when interpreting correlation coefficients and forecasting outcomes. Nevertheless the findings supported a correlation between the overall marks in the school-leaving examination and the annual Grade Point Averages, but this was mainly in the preclinical years.[2] None of the correlations between school-leaving marks and grades in medical school exceeded 0.4. The predictive value of school-leaving examinations therefore accounted for only 16 per cent of the variance in subsequent examinations.

These findings led us to conclude that selection of medical students on the basis of academic criteria alone is inadequate and should be accompanied by the assessment of their personal qualities. Experience particularly from Australia[3] with the measurement of personal qualities demonstrated that useful additional information can be provided by a structured interview and a proposal was made to our Faculty that such a process be instituted. In 1992 Faculty recommended 'this school no longer use school-leaving marks as the primary selection instrument. Measurement of personal qualities, motivation and life experiences by structured interviews should be combined with that of intellectual ability to rank applicants.'

Thinking about such a change is often easier than its implementation. However, as John Hunter wrote to Edward Jenner in 1779 in response to Jenner's questions on the life of the hedgehog: 'why think – why not try the experiment ... they will give you the solution.' The Auckland School has tried the experiment over the past four years and the changes which have been implemented and our initial experience with them will now be described.

The new selection process

Selection is based on the measurement of an applicant's academic ability and personal attributes. Academic ability is measured as previously by performance in the national school-leaving examination. The top academic 160 applicants are called for interview for the 80 places available in this category. The measurement of personal attributes is carried out by a structured panel interview, and a group exercise, supplemented by the secondary school principal's report.

The panel interview

The structured panel interview lasts twenty minutes and is carried out by a pair of interviewers, one a male and the other a female, one of whom must be medically qualified. These interviewers are not aware of the applicant's academic achievements. The non-academic attributes measured during the panel interviews by the pair of interviewers include maturity, caring qualities/friendliness, communication skills, an awareness of community issues and needs, certainty of career choice and involvement in school and community activities. Members of the panel are provided with a list of questions to help focus on these headings. For the past four years this interview has been repeated by a second panel.

The group exercise

The group exercise comprises six applicants participating in a skills assessment exercise which is observed by a new pair of observers, sitting at a distance. The exercise, which is designed to stimulate debate, involves the applicants sitting at a round table where they are asked to work as a team on some theoretical problem. One example is the ranking of six hypothetical applicants for the post of an appropriate doctor for a home for the elderly. This particular exercise lasts fifty minutes during which the panel assesses the discussion and scores each of the applicants on communication skills, listening skills, sensitivity/empathy, friendliness, organisational and leadership skills, and an awareness of community issues and needs.

The school principal's report

The final measurement of personal attributes is by means of a confidential assessment form sent to relevant school principals. This form seeks comments on the applicant's personal qualities under the headings communication skills – oral and written, maturity, personal qualities, involvement in sporting, cultural and community activities and an overall rating on qualities needed in a medical practitioner in the eyes of the principal.

The total personal assessment score is then calculated by adding together each of the subscores with the following weight: each panel interview 25 per cent, the group exercise 30 per cent, and the school report 20 per cent. Academic rank and personal assessment rank are given approximately equal weighting to form the final rank order from which places on the course are offered.

A review of our initial experience has not found a relationship between academic achievement as reflected by marks in a national school-leaving examination and the scores in the panel interviews, the group exercise or the school principal's report.[4] Significant intercorrelations were found however between the panel interviews, the group exercise and the school report.

Conclusion

Faculty members and university administrators expressed considerable apprehension concerning the introduction of methods to measure the personal qualities of applicants to medical school, especially in still maturing applicants. Our favourable initial experience has encouraged the School to continue to explore methods to measure personal attributes within a carefully controlled study.

In 1982 Paul Saunders wrote that 'Jenner had to clothe the bones of a countryside tradition about smallpox with the flesh of scientific proof.' There may be countryside perception of the need for inclusion of some measurement of personal attributes in the process of selection but it will require other schools to embark on the experiment in order to provide the scientific proof required. The recent encouragement by the General Medical Council (1993) and the World Summit on Medical Education (1994) of the development of selection procedures that explore non-academic attributes in addition to academic performance should help to advance this research.

References

1 Collins J P, White G R (1993) 'Selection of Auckland medical students over 25 years: a time for change?', *Medical Education*, 27, 321–27

2 Collins J P, White G R, Kennedy J A (1995) 'Entry to medical school: an audit of traditional selection requirements', *Medical Education*, 29, 22–28

3 Powis D A, Neame R L B, Bristow T & Murphy L B (1988) 'The objective structured interview for medical student selection', *British Medical Journal*, 296, 765–8

4 Collins J P, White G R, Petrie K J & Willoughby E (1995) 'A structured panel interview and group exercise in the selection of medical students', *Medical Education*, 29, 332–336

Discussion from the floor

A participant questioned whether in trying to select on a standard range of personal qualities there was a danger of losing some of the diversity of applicants to medicine, which needed many different types of people. John Collins agreed this was a potential problem, which had been discussed in an article by Lazarus in *Medical Teacher* in 1986. What was important is what was done with the ranking on academic criteria and the ranking on personal attributes. Using these two measurements could help to provide diversity depending upon a school's philosophy; Powis recently described in *Medical Education* (1994) the use of a formula which incorporated these different measurements.

It was noted that the drop-out rate from the Auckland course was the same for mature entrants as it was for school leavers. One participant thought that the drop-out rate in the UK from previously rejected applicants was probably very low, but data on this were unavailable, and the number of entrants to whom this might apply would be very small and make it difficult to give reliable conclusions.

In answer to a question about the fortunes of Maori medical students at Auckland, John Collins referred participants to a poster displayed at the meeting which summarised their experience and which was to be published shortly in *Medical Education*. An affirmative-action programme had been introduced in 1972 for those of Maori and Pacific Island background and there were now 12 places reserved for this scheme. Auckland had had to compete with other faculties for suitable applicants from the small pool available. One hundred and forty-seven such students had been admitted and 75 had graduated so far. The loss of students in this category was 18 per cent compared with 8 per cent for all remaining students. A further 35 students from the same ethnic group had been admitted through the normal selection process or outside the Affirmative Programme – these were the very bright applicants.

Noting that Auckland had about 650 applicants annually, and that 150–160 applicants were interviewed, a participant questioned whether the process described would be practicable in the UK, where numbers of applicants and places were greater (2,500–3,000 applicants for London medical schools).

The relationship of the structured interview score to the first two years' performance at Auckland was currently being analysed. The first intake via their new selection process were now in their fourth year. This cohort and the subsequent three were being studied by way of a communication skills assessment and by a questionnaire which measured personality and attitudes and by their academic progress. They were also being compared with two cohorts admitted through the previous system.

It was noted that there was poor agreement which criteria for being a good doctor should be used in selection, and that further research was needed in this area. One paper (Price, *Annals of Surgery*, 1971) described 87 characteristics of a good physician and this had subsequently been modified by Sade (1985) in the same journal where he ranked the most important 25. These were included in the Auckland selection criteria.

Discussion concluded on the topic of breadth of studies both previous to and following medical school. The narrowness of UK medical applicants' previous studies was noted, and that medical studies were often sharply differentiated from other higher education subjects, for example by encouraging students to put only these on their UCAS form rather than a range of subjects. John Collins reported that in Auckland there were no required subjects of prior study to enter the medical school, and that students who dropped out of medical school often moved to study in other faculties.

From Selection to Qualification: How and Why Medical Students Change

Chris McManus

Although I would like to start by showing a different portrait of Jenner from those already shown by the other speakers, I admit to having found the same marvellous quotation as that already used by John Collins, from Jenner's strangely eccentric piece in *The Artist*. As far as I can tell, it is Jenner's only piece of non-immunological writing. That is a great relief to me since, due to a quirk of my medical education in Cambridge and Birmingham, I managed to go through medical school without ever studying immunology, and therefore I was glad I did not have to struggle through the immunological papers. Jenner's paper in *The Artist* of Saturday July 18th 1807 cannot be claimed to have a snappy title. Let me quote it in full:

> *Classes of the Human Powers of Intellect – Hints for a Classification of the Powers of the Mind as they appear in various Descriptions of Men – Examples of Excellence rare – General Division into seven Classes – Difficulty of analysing all the Varieties of Intellect.*

I doubt if any journal editor would accept that nowadays, never mind that the paper contains no empirical data at all. And as John Collins has already said, the classification is not quite as sophisticated as that of modern psychology (although I guess that neither was Jenner's immunology as sophisticated as that of modern immunology). Jenner firstly classifies human intellect into seven groups:

1   *The Idiot*
2   *The Dolt*
3   *Mediocrity*
4   *Mental Perfection*
5   *Eccentricity*
6   *Insanity*
7   *The Maniac*

I am not particularly interested in the first two, the idiot and the dolt, or the last two, the insane and the maniac, but the three in the middle are of more relevance to our present purpose. By Mental Perfection, Jenner is, as we shall see, referring to some sort of Renaissance person, although it is implicitly recognised that most individuals will fall short of this paragon in one way or another:

> *If we subdivided mental perfection into six modifications, three of them might partake more or less of the quality attributed to No. 3 in the scale [Mediocrity]; and the other three, of the quality attributed to No. 5 [Eccentricity]....*

That is, if in selection we search for perfection then we will mostly err one way or the other. How does Jenner define Mental Perfection, Mediocrity and Eccentricity? Let us look at his pen sketches, which show also his fine way with the English language, and probably also reveal so much about Jenner the man. Let us start with Mediocrity:

> Mediocrity – *the large mass of mankind. These crowd our streets, these line our files, these cover our seas. It is with this class that the world is peopled. These are they who move constantly in the beaten path; these support the general order which they do not direct; these uphold the tumult which they do not stir; these echo the censure or praise of what they are neither capable of criticising or admiring.*

I presume that this is the class of individuals whom selection is trying to exclude from our medical schools as far as possible. Presumably what we want instead is Mental Perfection, described here by Jenner, trailing clouds of glories:

> Mental Perfection – *the happy union of all the faculties of the mind, which conduce to promote present and future good; all the energies of genius, valour, judgement. In this class are found the*

> *men who surveying truth in all her loveliness, defend her from*
> *assault, and unveil her charms to the world; who rule mankind*
> *by their wisdom, and contemplate glory, as the Eagle fixes his*
> *view on the sun, undazzled by the rays that surround it.*

Who could turn down such a person when their application form arrived? The danger of course, as Jenner has already suggested, is that Mental Perfection readily slides either into Mediocrity or, perhaps even worse, into the next category, of Eccentricity:

> Eccentricity – *with all its pleasant and unpleasant concomi-*
> *tants: comprehending all such men as are distinguished for*
> *great peculiarities – high flights of fancy – unsteadiness of*
> *character; – ungovernable either by the advice or admonition*
> *of friends; strangers to discretion; for the most part highly irrita-*
> *ble; always in extremes of conduct, extravagantly generous and*
> *benevolent, or miserably penurious: – who excite the wonder,*
> *the laughter or the contempt of the world.*

And recognising the numerical size of the problem, Jenner adds, in a lovely little one-liner, 'I have in this class a very numerous acquaintance'.

Jenner's categories clearly define the problem of medical selection in general: to find as many individuals as possible with Mental Perfection, while weeding out the Mediocre and the Eccentric. How do we do it? Indeed, can we do it?

Differences between medical schools in selection

In the main part of this paper I want to describe some studies we have carried out over the past fifteen or so years, and to look at three separate sorts of question. I will start with the question of whether there are differences between entrants to medical schools which interview candidates and those which do not. In the UK we have a natural experiment which ought to allow us to answer this question because some medical schools interview and some do not. On the basis of such a comparison I would like to develop a simple but, I think, very informative theoretical model of the practical limits of selection, which will, I hope, make us realise that we are seriously constrained in what we have any realistic hope of achieving by selection. And then in the third part of my paper I want to look at some outcome measures, in the fairly traditional form of basic science and final examinations, as well as in terms of clinical experience, which is an outcome measure that has not previously been studied very much.

The results I will be describing are based on three studies which have been carried out at St Mary's Medical School since 1980 in collaboration with Peter Richards, who was fundamental in initiating this research and in supporting it in so many ways over the years. Table 1 summarises our three separate cohort studies which examined applicants who entered medical schools in 1981, 1986 and 1991. In the first two studies we looked only at people who had applied to St Mary's, although, of course, since most applicants applied to four or five other medical schools, the majority actually entered other UK medical schools. So I must emphasise very strongly that we are not looking only at people who entered St Mary's, but at people who entered any UK medical school. For our 1991 cohort we had the cooperation of four other medical schools in England (University College London, the United Medical and Dental Schools, the University of Sheffield and the University of Newcastle-upon-Tyne). We are very grateful for their assistance, not least because of the large increase in sample size that resulted. The applicants applied in 1980, 1985 or 1990, were admitted in 1981, 1986 and 1991 and qualified in 1986, 1991 and 1996 (or 1987, 1992 and 1997 if they took an inter-calated degree). The 1991 cohort is still being studied in its final year at the present. To give you some idea of the numbers involved, there were about 1,400 applicants in the first study, and nearly 7,000 in the last one, with about 500, 800 and almost 3,000 entrants to medical school. So we do have quite decent sample sizes.

Let us start by looking at the question of medical schools which interview candidates. In 1991 when we carried out our survey there were 28 medical schools in Britain of which twenty were interviewing and eight were non-interviewing, by which I mean that they did not interview the majority of their entrants. The non-interviewing schools were Leeds, *Manchester, Southampton, Aberdeen, Dundee, Edinburgh, St. Andrews, and Belfast. The asterisk against Manchester indicates that it has since become an interviewing school, which is an important and interesting change. You will notice that no London school is non-interviewing but that lots of Scottish schools do not interview, with Glasgow as the only interviewing school in Scotland. Belfast is like other schools in Ireland in that it does not interview. This means that medical schools who choose not to interview represent a very non-random set of schools in general.

Our primary interest was in whether entrants to interviewing schools differ systematically from those at non-interviewing schools. Although it may seem that is a very straightforward question to ask, in statistical terms it actually becomes exceedingly subtle methodologically, and it has vexed my mind for a long while. The principal

Table 1: Shows brief details of the three cohort studies of medical student selection and training, and emphasises the time scale over which such studies must necessarily work if they are to follow individuals throughout their working life.

	1981 cohort[2,6-8]	*1986 cohort*[2,9]	*1991 cohort*[10]
Applicants to:	St Mary's	St Mary's	St Mary's, UMDS, UCL, Sheffield, Newcastle-upon-Tyne
Entrants to:	Any UK school	Any UK school	Any UK school
Applied:	1980	1985	1990
Entered:	1981	1986	1991
Qualified:	1986/87	1991/92	1996/97
5 years post-qualification	1991/92	1996/97	2001/02
10 years post-qualification	1996/97	2001/02	2006/07
20 years post-qualification	2006/07	2011/12	2016/17
30 years post-qualification	2016/17	2021/22	2026/27
Applicants in study	1,478	2,399	6,901
% UK applicants	12.6%	24.7%	~71%
Entrants	517	871	2,962
% UK entrants	12.9%	22.7%	69.7%

problem is that applicants apply both to interviewing and non-interviewing schools and they receive offers from a combination of them, and that makes it quite difficult to tease apart what is going on. In what follows I will be referring only to our 1991 study since it is much the largest and therefore the most suitable for this analysis; and in addition it also has the widest range of measures.

Analysis

In our analysis we did two separate things. First we compared entrants to interviewing and non-interviewing schools; and secondly we looked at those applicants who received offers from interviewing and non-interviewing schools (although, of course, just because an applicant receives an offer does not mean that he or she will enter medical school). So it is quite possible to find differences at one stage and not at the other stage. What sort of measures were we using? We had extensive data on these students. We sent them all a detailed 16 page questionnaire to complete and managed to achieve a 93 per cent response rate, which is a tribute both to the commitment of the applicants and the tenacity of my research assistants. As a result we had a wide range of information on these applicants (see Table 2).

First we looked at our demographic measures, many of which are not of particular interest for our present purposes but which we knew were probably predictors of success, and hence we wanted them to be in the analysis. We also looked at educational qualifications, including mean A-level grades and the number of A-levels taken, as well as the pattern of A-levels taken, in particular whether applicants had taken A-levels in a language, an arts subject and so on; and we did similar analyses for GCSE results. 18 separate sub-measures went into the analysis at this point.

We also wanted to look at the broader aspect of people's attitudes, their personal characteristics and so on, because I presume that it is such attributes that interviewing schools would like to think they are assessing. We looked at two separate sets of measures. One set related to what we can call attitudes to medicine and included such items as the age at which the decision was made to study medicine; attitudes to things like AIDS, to disability, to professional help; and to problems in themselves; to encouragements to study medicine; and to interests in the medical course, in particular medical careers; on motivations for studying medicine; and on a doctor-centred or patient-centred approach. In other words, we looked at a wide range of the sorts of things that one may feel could potentially be picked up by an interview. We also had a second set of measurements which were more psychological than medical, and were mainly to do with personality and individual differences; they included a set of timed IQ tests on many applicants who came for interview, measures of attitudes, social, ethical, and political, a decision-making questionnaire, a self-completion questionnaire on empathy, locus of control and so on. Table 2 summarises the breadth of our measures. I would particularly point out that we had a timed test called the Profile of Non-verbal Sensitivity (PONS) where subjects had to watch a video and then say what emotion or situations the person in the video was portraying. Overall, as Table 2 shows, we used a lot of measures.

The important results from this analysis are very simple. The crucial result is that there is no evidence that interviewing medical schools in Britain are admitting candidates who differ systematically

Table 2 The various measures included in the comparison of applicants and entrants to interviewing and non-interviewing schools. Figures in parentheses indicate the number of sub-scales on each measure.

Demographic measures:	*Personality and individual differences*
Date of application (1)	AH5 verbal & spatial ability (2)
Ethnic minority (1)	Attitudes [Social, ethical, political] (8)
Mature (1)	Decision making (7)
Medical family (1)	Empathy (4)
North of England (1)	Locus of control (3)
Post A-level (1)	Masculinity-Femininity (1)
Previous application (1)	Personality type (6)
Private sector education (1)	Profile of Non-verbal Sensitivity
Social Class (1)	[PONS] (3)
	Reading breadth (1)
Educational qualifications:	Sensation seeking (1)
A-level grades & subjects (9)	Sex-role attitudes (1)
GCSE/O-level grades & subjects (18)	Social behaviour (4)
	State anxiety (1)
Attitudes to Medicine	Study habits/Learning style (4)
Age decided to be a doctor (2)	Tolerance of ambiguity (1)
Attitudes to AIDS (1)	Type A behaviour (1)
Attitudes to disability (3)	
Attitudes to professional help (5)	
Encouragements for medicine (13)	
Interests in medical course (6)	
Medical career interests (7)	
Motivation for studying medicine (3)	
Patient-centredness (1)	

on these non-academic measures. They differ on A-level grades, but that is all, and I cannot convince myself that there is any other systematic difference between the groups.

That negative result does not mean that we must entirely abandon the idea that interviews do anything. I still believe they do something, although I know I might be seen to be flying in the face of many years of evidence in the psychological literature which says that they do very little or perhaps nothing. In part they do a number of things which we have not considered, one of which we have data on but which I can only mention very briefly. We carried out an analysis on what happens when an applicant holds two offers, one at an interviewing school and one at a non-interviewing school. All other things being equal one would expect a 50/50 chance of the applicant choosing the interviewing school, whereas in fact on 70 per cent of occasions they actually chose the interviewing school. So I think interviewing does something in encouraging candidates actually to come to a school, even if it does not necessarily bring different candidates. There is also the possibility, which we have not looked at yet, that entrants to interviewing schools may behave differently at medical school or they may become different types of doctors; those are questions still to be studied. We have not got the outcome measures for that at the moment and it is quite possible that the differences will appear later. And it is also possible, although I have not measured it yet, that interviewing may be important because it alters the attitudes of staff. They feel an ownership and involvement in the process of selection so that when the students come they do not say, 'Good heavens, what have they sent to us this year?' but instead staff have to say, 'We chose these people; therefore let us help them and support them'.

In order to understand what may or may not be going on in interviewing I need, at this point, to become more theoretical and ask how we can model the process of student selection, and I will describe a model first developed with Dr Charles Vincent[1]. First, consider what happens if we have a single selection criterion and that criterion is distributed in the population in a normal distribution. And to keep it simple, imagine that we want to select exactly half of the people applying. In fact such a selection ratio, of 2:1, is pretty well what actually happens if we look at the British system overall: half of those applying are eventually accepted.

Figure 1 shows that the simplest, and statistically the optimal, method is to choose those at the top half of the distribution. In other words, those above the mean are accepted, and those below the mean are rejected. Now such a method is fine if you only have *one* selection criterion, and we do at least have that in the sense that most people believe that academic ability in the form of A-levels must be of some importance in student selection.

Now, the situation gets more interesting if, instead of selecting on just one criterion, we select on two or more. If we select on two criteria then we have a graph that looks like Figure 2, in other words a bivariate normal distribution, which we are, as it were, looking down on from above. Ability 1 goes from bad to good and ability 2 also goes from less good through to better. Assume that the selection ratio still remains the same as before, so that we are looking for 50 per cent of the applicants. If we wish to select them so that each selected candidate is above a certain minimum on each of the two distributions, then those selected will lie in a 'square' in the top right hand corner of the distribution, indicated by the two solid lines. In identifying the position of this square, something important happens in comparison with the situation when we selected on just one criterion so that we cut the distribution at the mean, exactly at its mid-point, with *half* lying

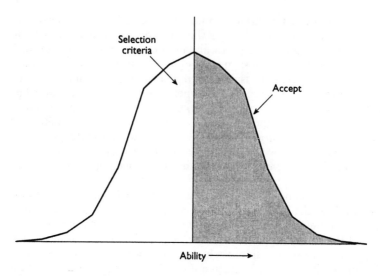

Figure 1 Selection based on a single ability, with the criterion set so that the top 50% are selected.

above the mean. With two uncorrelated criteria, however, if we cut each criterion at its mean then, of necessity, we would only have selected *a quarter* of the candidates. In other words, to select half of the candidates then we must select those in the top 70 per cent or so of each distribution, meaning that the cutting point on each selection criterion will be *substantially below the mean.*

The situation becomes more extreme as more possible selection criteria are invoked (and at today's meeting many people have called for perhaps dozens of factors to be taken into account in selecting those Leonardos who will eventually be able to call themselves Doctor – indeed, John Collins referred to perhaps 80 or 90 separate selection criteria). What happens to selection on each criterion as the number of selection criteria increases? Table 3 shows the proportion of people rejected on each single criterion as the number of criteria increases. By the time you are selecting on ten criteria you are only rejecting the bottom 6 or 7 per cent on each criterion, and if you try and select on 50 criteria then you are only actually rejecting the bottom 1.5 per cent on any of those criteria.

There are two strong implications to come from such an analysis. Firstly, and I cannot emphasise it enough, *if you select on everything you are actually selecting on nothing.* In effect, you are only weeding out a very small number of the weirdos at the very bottom of each distribution,

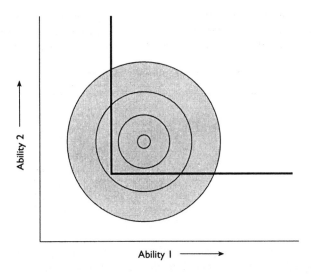

Figure 2 Selection based on two abilities which are assumed to be uncorrelated and distributed as a bivariate normal (viewed from above). In order to select 50% of candidates with all of them above a particular threshold on each ability the candidates must be in the top right hand corner indicated by the two solid lines. Note that both of these lines are below the mean on each ability.

and you are having little impact on the distributions as a whole, and the mean of those selected will be almost the same as for those in the population as a whole. So one is on the horns of a vicious dilemma, one which is fundamentally mathematical, and one which I suspect has barely been taken into account at this meeting, and must be considered by any calls for a massive increase in the range of selection criteria. There is also an important corollary to this principle of selection, and that is that if one over-emphasises the importance of selection on one factor, let us say it is A-level grades, then no room at all is left for selection on any other factors. Thus in Figure 2, if you insist on taking only those who are above average on criterion 1 then there can be no selection at all on criterion 2 if you are to take only half of the subjects. At this point I hope that the relevance of this theoretical model to the role of interviewing in British medical schools is becoming apparent. If indeed A-levels are overly dominant in student selection then there is almost no variance left to be accounted for by other selection methods such as interviewing. So the next empirical question we must look at is the extent to which A-levels are indeed a useful and satisfac-

Table 3 Shows the proportion of candidates who would be rejected on the basis of a particular criterion (criterion 1) according to the number of other independent criteria on which selection is also being carried out.

Number of selection criteria	Candidates rejected on criterion 1
1	Bottom 50%
2	Bottom 29%
3	Bottom 21%
4	Bottom 16%
5	Bottom 13%
6	Bottom 11%
10	Bottom 6.7%
20	Bottom 3.4%
50	Bottom 1.4%

tory predictor of appropriate outcomes during medical training. In other words, to ask whether their dominance in selection is justified.

A-levels as predictors of performance

How good actually are A-levels at predicting performance during undergraduate medical training? I will start by looking at examination results in medical school. Although examination results are far from being everything, there is some logic in starting with exams since ultimately there is no point in selecting people who are not going to qualify. It is a waste of our time and their time, and even if they are the nicest people in the world they do need to be able to attain the necessary standards of competence. I will begin by looking at the 1991 cohort, which is our largest study, and for which we have recently put together some preliminary results on the performance of the students on their basic medical science courses. At this point I must thank the Registrars of the various medical schools who have been invaluable in helping us to follow up the students in our cohort studies. We could not have done the work without them. We are here describing the follow-up of about 2,800 entrants to UK medical schools for whom at present we have adequate follow-up information. Our classification of outcome is necessary fairly crude since the students are in all the different medical schools in the UK, with their host of different examining methods, and hence we could not do anything terribly subtle. Nevertheless we feel our classification is effective and useful.

We divided the students into those who had left medical school either of their own accord or as a result of exam failure, those who had been required to repeat a year at some point, those who had passed in their basic medical science exams but only after taking one or more resits, those who had got through without any resits and those who achieved distinction, had been awarded a prize, or something similar. The students are also divided according to their average A-level grade (irrespective of the number of A-levels taken), ranging from those with an average of three As, through those with an average of three Bs, to those with an average of three Cs and those with less than three Cs (and you will see in Figure 3 that the number in the latter category is very small, as one would expect amongst current medical students).

The category across the top of the graph is those with a distinction or prize, and there is little doubt that they are more common amongst those with the highest A-level grades. There also seems a clear trend for those who are failing, across the bottom category of the graph, to be rather more common amongst those with the lowest A-level grades. And parallel trends are found for those in the intermediate groups. So we can certainly conclude that A-levels are successful in predicting something useful. At that point it might be tempting to say that A-levels *are* a good selection criterion and to carry on using them as our principal, or perhaps only, form of selection. The problem with that position is that A-levels are not quite such a

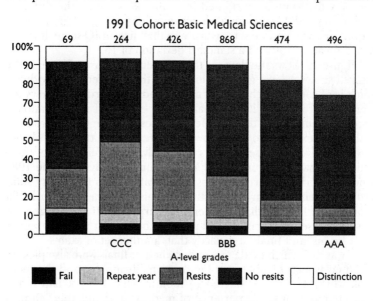

Figure 3 Performance of candidates in the 1991 cohort on their basic medical sciences examinations, in relation to A-level grades.

such a strong criterion as they look at first sight. Although you have to be careful because the number of individuals in each of the groups differs, notice that the vast majority of the students are in the top four A-level groups, and therefore despite people in the bottom two groups failing proportionately more often, most of the students who fail actually have good grades. Although there is a higher proportion of those who are failing in the lowest grades, the majority of people who are leaving are actually entering medical school with high A-level grades. So A-levels are not terribly good at predicting actual losses, although there is undoubtedly a correlation present: as the epidemiologists would say, there is a low attributable risk from having lower A-level grades.

What about final examinations? In the 1981 and 1986 cohort we were very lucky because at that time in the University of London there was a standard set of examinations which almost all medical students took. Those at the Royal Free and St George's had a different system, and I have excluded them from the present analysis. We sorted through the archives to find out how the students in our study had performed in their final examinations, either in 1986 or 1987 for the 1981 entrants, or 1991 or 1992 for the 1986 entrants. We calculated examination performance as a single score, which was approximately normally distributed, calculated from the marks in all the different finals exams, be they multiple choice questions, essays, clinical examinations or vivas, and we set this score so that, like an IQ score, it would have a mean of 100 and a standard deviation of 15.

Figure 4a shows the data for the 1981 entrants. As in Figure 3, the abscissa shows A-level grades, along with the number of individuals, which is of course much smaller in this study. The ordinate shows the average performance in the final exams, expressed as the standard score. It is quite clear that as A-level grades increase so performance in the final examinations improves; and remember that the A-levels were taken five, six or seven years previously. The replicability of these results is shown in Figure 4b, which is a similar analysis for the 1986 cohort, and the pattern is almost identical. So this is a pretty solid result: A-levels are clearly predictive of finals examinations over half a decade later. Perhaps that is not entirely surprising. If you are good at passing one set of exams you will probably be good at passing another set of exams, and finals are exactly that, another set of exams.

It was that which made us wonder whether finals were also picking up other aspects of what is going on in medicine, beyond the mere book work, and so we started to look at what I think is a much neglected area of the experience of medical students, their clinical experience. What do they actually do? How many patients do they

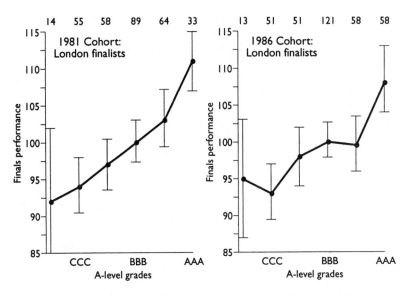

Figure 4 Performance in London final examinations of students in a) the 1981 cohort and b) the 1986 cohort, in relation to A-level grades.

see, how much do they do things to them, watch things being done to them, and so on? And so instead of just looking at performance on final exams we tried to measure the clinical experience of the students. We used a questionnaire given to the students about three months before their final exams, which asked them about their experience of twenty medical conditions, eighteen surgical operations, and twenty-nine practical procedures. We asked them to indicate how often they had seen the medical conditions, how often they had seen surgical operations, and for practical procedures whether they had seen them, performed them with supervision, or performed them alone. We found a wide overall range in the clinical experience, and we combined the three different types of experience into a total score which is what we will consider here, although it must be said that the results are similar for all three measures. The wide range of clinical experience means that some people are seeing a lot of patients, and therefore getting a lot of experience, whereas others are seeing few patients and thus gaining little experience. We take it as given that it is desirable that students should see a lot of patients and experience a wide range of procedures.

The first question we need to consider is whether A-levels can

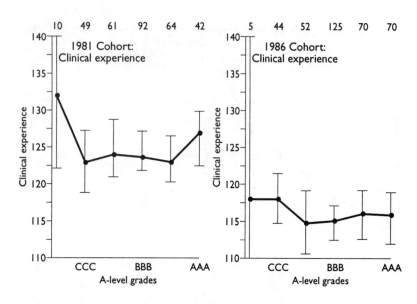

Figure 5 Clinical experience in the final clinical years of students in a) the 1981 cohort and b) the 1986 cohort, in relation to A-level grades.

predict the extent of that clinical experience. Figure 5a shows, for the 1981 cohort, the overall clinical experience on the ordinate in relation to A-level grades on the abscissae and, as in Figures 4a and 4b, I have plotted the ordinate so that its range consists of one standard deviation above and below the mean so that the figures are comparable. Whatever else A-levels are doing, it is clear that they are not predicting which students are gaining a lot of experience, and which are only gaining a little. Figure 5b shows exactly the same pattern, with the only difference that the 1986 line is significantly below the 1981 line, which reflects a genuine fall in the amount of clinical experience that students are reporting over that five year period[2]. But that is another issue altogether.

We also asked whether performance in final examinations related to clinical experience, because one would like to think that good examinations would be assessing clinical behaviour, and hence that those with a greater amount of clinical experience should do better in their finals. That resulted in an important finding, which is potentially problematic. In both the 1981 and the 1986 cohorts, the correlation between the amount of clinical experience and performance in finals was pretty well zero. And more distressing still was that experience of surgical operations did not correlate with performance in the surgical exam, nor experience of medical conditions with performance in the medicine exam. That forced us to ask some broader questions about clinical experience, and in particular, to ask whether any other measures correlated with it or could predict it. We had long been interested in an area which educational psychologists refer to as study habits or learning styles, and which we suspected might well relate to clinical experience.

Study habits

Study habits can be divided into three broad types, which are called surface, deep and strategic, which differ according to the motivations of the students for studying and the process by which they carry out their study. Surface learners are motivated in order to complete the course, which is all they really care about and they are particularly concerned with avoiding failure. They process information principally by rote learning of facts, and they focus on specific tasks in isolation, not really caring about content itself, but seeing factual material merely as the way to pass exams. They are typical of students who learn, regurgitate and then forget. By contrast, deep learners are motivated by an interest in the subject itself and often by the vocational relevance of material, and by a need for personal understanding. They study by relating ideas to evidence, they integrate material across courses and they identify general principles. Finally, strategic learners are a combination of surface and deep, being driven by a need for success. They love to compete with others and their real motivation is to get high grades, and they use whatever study techniques achieve the highest grades, which might mean surface learning for some topics and deep learning for others, resulting in an understanding which is often extremely patchy and variable.

Do study habits correlate with clinical experience? We might expect they do, particularly given the importance of vocational relevance in deep learners. Table 4 shows for our two cohorts the correlation of study habits in the final year with clinical experience. Greater clinical experience correlates positively with strategic and deep learning, and negatively with surface learning. In other words, those with the right motivations for learning (and I use the word 'right' in a strict sense since I think the surface learners are wrong in objective terms), were the ones seeing the most patients. So clinical experience does correlate with something, but it is not final examination performance or A-levels. Much more interesting though is that we had also measured surface, deep and strategic learning at the time

Table 4 Correlation of clinical experience measured in the final year with study habits/learning style measured in the final year and at application to medical school.

Final year	1981 (n=333)	1986 (n=375)
Surface	−0.073	−0.054
Deep	0.212 p<0.001	0.136 p<0.001
Strategic	0.206 p<0.001	0.213 p<0.001

Applicants	1981 (n=311)	1986 (n=363)
Surface	−0.134 p<0.05	−0.140 p<0.01
Deep	na	0.262 p<0.001
Strategic	na	0.220 p<0.001

of selection, five and six years earlier, and Table 4 shows that the correlations are pretty well indistinguishable from the measures we took in the final year. In other words, by a questionnaire measure taken at selection we can predict who is going to be seeing a lot of patients, will be going to theatre a lot and will be doing a lot of practical procedures five or six years later.

At this point you may be concerned that perhaps if nothing else, study habits are predicted by A-level grades, so let me disabuse you of that notion very quickly. There is simply no correlation between study habits and A-level grades. So by selecting on A-levels we are not selecting people with deep and strategic study habits. That is probably because there are two very different ways of getting good grades at A-level, either by learning a lot of facts or by understanding, and the method of examining necessarily cannot distinguish easily between them.

Conclusions

I have now reached the end of a complex chain of argument, so let me try and put it together and summarise the conclusions. I started by saying that interviewing and non-interviewing schools do not seem to select different students and my suspicion is that this is probably due to an undue emphasis in the system on A-level grades which leaves little room for selection on the basis of other characteristics. A-level grades are not entirely unimportant. They do predict performance on basic medical science and clinical examinations but they are far from perfect in doing that. Nevertheless we obviously cannot throw them out completely, and it might well be that in part their relatively poor performance as predictors is due to restriction of range, there being few people in medical school with three E grades.

More worrying is that clinical experience, which I would regard as fundamental to being a good doctor, since it is only by seeing a lot of patients that you can learn from them, is not related to A-levels, and also worryingly, clinical experience is not related to performance in finals. Clinical experience is however related to study habits, both in the final year and at selection, but as far as I can tell at present, appropriate study habits are not being selected for in our selection systems at present. The result is that by mainly selecting on A-levels alone, we are not selecting those students who are going to gain most clinical experience. The end result is that if we really want to try and select on the basis of other desirable characteristics that have been identified, and I think learning style is certainly one of them, we have to bite the bullet and say we are going to accept somewhat lower A-level grades so that we have the room to manoeuvre in order actually to be able to select on the other important characteristics.

References

1   McManus I C, Vincent C A (1993) Selecting and educating safer doctors. In: Vincent CA, Ennis M, Audley RJ, eds. *Medical accidents*, Oxford: Oxford University Press

2   McManus I C Richards P, Winder B C, Sproston K A, Vincent C A (1993) The changing clinical experience of British medical students. *Lancet*; 341: 941-944

3   Parkhouse J (1996) Intake, output, and drop out in United Kingdom medical schools. *Brit Med J*; 312: 885

4   McManus I C (1996) Drop out rate in medical schools seems reasonable. *Brit Med J*; 313: 173

5   Biggs J B (1993) What do inventories of students' learning processes really measure? A theoretical review and clarification. *British Journal of Educational Psychology*; 63: 3-19.

6   McManus I C, Richards P (1984) An audit of admission to medical school: 1. Acceptances and rejects. *Brit Med J*; 289: 1201-1204.

7   McManus I C, Richards P (1986) Admission for medicine in the United Kingdom: a structural model. Med Educ; 20: 181-186.

8   McManus I C, Richards P (1986) Prospective survey of performance of medical students during preclinical years. *Brit Med J*; 293: 124-127.

9   McManus I C, Richards P, Maitlis S L (1989) Prospective study of the disadvantage of people from ethnic minority groups applying to medical schools in the United Kingdom. *Brit Med J*; 298: 723-726.

10   McManus I C, Richards P, Winder B C, Sproston K A, Styles V (1995)
     Medical school applicants from ethnic minorities: identifying if and
     when they are disadvantaged. *Brit Med J*; 310: 496–500.

Discussion from the floor

A speaker from the floor reflected that perhaps the most important factor was not so much the selection of medical students but what happened to them during the medical school course. She stressed the importance of support for medical students, particularly those who might feel that they had made the wrong decision in studying medicine but had valuable qualities such as maturity and sensitivity which were not necessarily easily measurable in straightforward academic terms. Chris McManus agreed that many of the attributes which were desirable in doctors, such as communication, empathy and sensitivity, were trainable skills, and that concentrating on selection as a way of avoiding problems was wrong.

Concern was expressed about drop-out from medical school and how this might be cut. Chris McManus commented that the drop-out rate was difficult to assess accurately and that, in any case, there were no objective national examination criteria for medical students. He noted the analysis by Parkhouse in the *British Medical Journal*[3] claiming a drop-out rate of 13 per cent. Chris McManus thought this was almost certainly too high since the proportion in his cohort studies was about 6–7 per cent[4], which was confirmed by independent General Medical Council data. This proportion was made up of about 3 per cent who failed their examinations and 3 per cent who chose not to carry on. He thought that these were reasonable proportions, and that the cost of medical education would not be fundamentally changed by reducing a 6 or 7 per cent drop-out rate to 2 or 3 per cent.

In response to another question, Chris McManus emphasised the point that the one characteristic that doctors needed, whichever specialty they were in, was the characteristic being picked up by the 'surface-deep-strategic' measures in his studies. He noted that if doctors were vocationally motivated, had an interest in understanding mechanisms and processes for their own sake, enjoyed what they did and were not merely motivated by fear of failure, then they were probably going to be the life-long learners, the reflective practitioners that everybody had said were needed in medicine.

It was possible to identify these characteristics before entry to medical school through using an 18 item questionnaire derived from the Biggs Study Process Questionnaire[5] with each item completed on a 5-point scale. However, Chris McManus pointed out that, although this was a reliable research measure, it was not necessarily a good selection instrument since the applicants could learn how to respond appropriately unless the instrument were disguised. He thought that this was not an insuperable problem but would need research and development – and resources. His suspicion was that the sort of group task described by John Collins might implicitly have been picking up components of deep and strategic learning without the students being aware of what was being assessed.

SUMMARY

Peter Richards

The importance of selection

Why is entry to medicine so controversial? Perhaps partly because it is an unusually highly sought-after course of study despite all the evidence that it is a tough and demanding career. But there are other courses which are very popular, veterinary medicine and law, for example, and there is not quite the same stir about selection of students in those professions. Perhaps it is because the public feel that the qualities of their doctors are particularly close to home. Selection, as we have been reminded, needs to be fair. Fair to applicants who may wrongly believe that academic ability confers a right to acceptance – speakers were prepared to challenge that right. Fair to the public, as individuals who may take a broader view of the desirable qualities of doctors, and to the public as a population with broader health needs. We cannot, of course, be fair to applicants who do not apply. That is a very big subject on which we hardly touched and for which the medical schools, I think, only bear a very small responsibility.

Selection also needs to be good for the nation, which may wish to ensure that medical science and medical research goes forward as part of national responsibility and opportunity. We have been reminded that selection needs to be as objective and open as possible, and we have come up hard against the question of 'selection for what?' In a very diverse profession the skills required to be a good doctor in one part of it might be very different from those required in another. We have also been challenged with the need to select and train doctors appropriate for the changing health care demands of the future. John Collins gave us a quotation from Shaw, to which we might add: 'Up to a certain point doctors, like masons and carpenters, must earn their living doing work that the public wants from them'.

Positive aspects of current selection

There are several positive points which should be made about the students we select currently. Firstly, medicine, despite the stress and strain, has about the lowest wastage rate of any university course. Medical students are real people, who change their minds, become diverted or even become ill, but they do it less than students in other disciplines. I consider that a 6 per cent wastage rate during medical school is irreducible – this reflects that medical students are just normal people. Wastage after qualification is perhaps a larger and more challenging problem. Secondly, medicine is the one university discipline in which women graduate maintaining their relative academic superiority over men. Most other courses seem to blunt the academic edge of women. Thirdly, we have been reminded that when students graduate and become doctors they go into a profession which, for all its faults, gives a higher satisfaction rate to the public, than any other profession or any other walk of life. A satisfaction rate of over 80 per cent compares well with policemen, who rate about 50 per cent, lawyers 30 per cent and politicians, about 5 per cent. That of course is not to say that there is no room for improvement. The course is becoming more patient-centred and postgraduate training is becoming more professional.

Broadening the selection criteria

John Collins recommended broadening the effective criteria, particularly in moving away from a narrow school-leaving exam ranking, and he described one approach to the measurement of desirable non-academic attributes. However, the process of fair, appropriate, reliable and valid selection is immensely complicated, as Chris McManus showed us. It is indeed a science in itself and it was sobering to have explained to us that if you select on everything you select on nothing. 'Truth in all her loveliness,' which Chris quoted from Jenner's one irreverent paper, is clearly some way off.

I was grateful some years ago to Chris for introducing me to a paper by Sir James Paget who studied the outcome of the training of a thousand students at Barts in the middle of the last century. Paget concluded, after a great deal of work over many years, that 'nothing appears more certain than that the personal character, the very nature,' (by which perhaps he meant attitude) 'the will of each student had far greater force on determining his career than any helps or hindrances'. He did not venture to say whether the curriculum was a help or hindrance. We need to define and to find reliable ways of identifying desirable personal characteristics, desirable for a wide range of professional outcomes. Very good arguments were put forward for making these assessments later rather than sooner, and I think many of us would be very pleased to select medical students over the age of 21. There are enormous practical difficulties with this in terms of the financing; nevertheless, graduate schools for medicine should remain on the agenda.

Desirable characteristics in selection

Joe Collier gave us the usually accepted list of the desirable characteristics of a doctor. Others were mentioned elsewhere which are often missed, such as curiosity: curiosity in the context of scholarship but also, we might say, curiosity about career opportunity. Medical students, in my long experience, are their own worst enemies in being reluctant to think about what they are going to do when they qualify. They are so focused on qualifying. The ability to cope was referred to twice: Sally Greengross mentioned coping with other people's problems, and Robert Hale referred to coping too with one's own anxieties. There should also be the ability to live with uncertainty and to live with one's mistakes. Joe Collier mentioned respect for others. Kenneth Calman referred to the broad context and widest sphere of background that is so valuable and often missing, to the need to be capable of developing a trusting relationship and the need to be resilient. The resilience referred to was in context of all the psychological stresses and strains and Robert Hale pointed in this regard to the importance of an institution being supportive. Extending that thought, we should also look for medical students who are able and willing to contribute to a vibrant, supportive, inspiring, constructively critical environment in which they learn together. They learn an enormous amount from each other and can create absolutely the right environment.

Conclusion

At the beginning of the conference William Asscher awarded St George's a bouquet for getting it right with Jenner. However, he did not mention that the student was introduced to the Dean by his father or that the number of applicants on that occasion was just one. Nor that the qualification was a standard apprenticeship for which the fee of 100 guineas for board, lodging and tuition was payable not to St George's Hospital Medical School but to the surgeon personally. That fee makes today's overseas student fee look modest by comparison.

Despite all these considerations and his unashamedly middle class background, Jenner – inspired and encouraged by Hunter – was a star.

But whether or not St George's deserves much credit for Jenner, it does deserve both credit and our thanks for organising this symposium which has opened up, even if it has not been able to solve, the questions of whether we can do even better in choosing tomorrow's doctors than today's. I believe that there is much right but of course something wrong with today's doctors. Tomorrow's require not necessarily a different group of individuals but a more challenging and perhaps a more appropriate education, and a better deal in specialist education and training, which is now happening through the Calman proposals for specialist training.